A BOOK OF SELF RE-EDUCATION

Raden Ayou Jodjana.
© George Verkuil

A Book of Self Re-Education

THE STRUCTURE AND FUNCTIONS
OF THE HUMAN BODY
AS AN INSTRUMENT OF EXPRESSION

RADEN AYOU JODJANA

L. N. FOWLER & CO. LTD.
1201/3 High Road
Chadwell Heath
Romford RM6 4DH
Essex

SBN 85243 364 6

Printed in Great Britain at
The Camelot Press Ltd, Southampton

Contents

The teaching of Raden Ayou Jodjana which appears in
"A BOOK OF RE-EDUCATION"
is available in a set of three cassettes

Introduction

In our book are published the results
of a life-long research:
the structure and functions of the human body
as an instrument of expression.
We made a study of the nervous system,
including the brain,
and of its basic intellectual functions of attention.
We also studied the functions of the centre of gravity,
especially its space functions,
and how it creates perfect balance in the form.
We found that the centre of gravity co-ordinates all other functions.
Attention was also given to the functions
of the central muscle, the diaphragm,
which translates psychic tensions into physical tensions.

Space

O Space, thy holy essence,
embracing all and interpenetrating
all form.

Thou gentle liberator, setting us free
from all that seems to bind us,
carrying us on wings ethereal.

Thou most compassionate, forever present,
being at-one with all that is,
essence of truth, revealing
through the fabric of illusions of our human life,
that deepest consciousness of pure perfection.

In thee, there cannot be that cruel separation
threatening us through the perverted consciousness of limitation.

For all thy working is relationship most intimate,
the perfect unity of all things.
O Space, thy tenderness is infinite.

Starting on Self Re-education by a Book

Starting on self re-education by a book
is in itself a hazardous undertaking.
We hope and wish to open to everyone
the possibility of inner research,
carried by the gentle support of inspiration.

You will notice that many poems have no title.
I will tell you why.
When we teach the different exercises
we execute them ourselves
while we tell how to set out
on a trace in space,
mostly *inside* our bodies.
We lead the pupils on these tracks,
and they start on the way fully alive and open,
without the mental fixation of obtaining a result.
But we noticed that they were in the habit
of fixing in their minds
the aim they wished to reach.
A habit which they should give up altogether.

Giving our full attention to what took place in them,
we discovered that mentally they had already arrived
where they still had to go.
So moving, they find themselves in a no-man's-land,
and are not open to impressions and experiences on the way.
They become like a machine.
They are attracted by their fixed aim ahead.
Already they are there,
in their mind acting and speaking.
They no longer feel
the inner urge of their original intention.
We then set out with the pupils on research,
asking them to become aware in every moment
of the *movement of searching*;
in order to discover and live some inner experience
they did not feel and know before.

The mind's wonderful capacity of attention
should be still, and open, and not preoccupied
constructing mental pictures.
This wrong habit is so strong in most people,
that when we lead them
to a certain place inside the body,
to feel clearly the structure of an organ,
even having already lived this experience with us
they will invent a mental picture or a term.
They fix the experience,
and then start to discuss the results amongst themselves.
Repeating the exercise,
the experience will wear out.

May the Book I am Writing

May the book I am writing,
as Inayat Khan told me to do,
be accepted as he hoped it would.
And may it become a special basis
on which Western people
can re-educate themselves;
and understand the message
Inayat Khan tried to bring to them
in the language of music.

Just as my husband, Raden Mas Jodjana,
came to the West with the same message.
But to be given out in the language
of pure movement,
creating the same inner silence
as music.

How to use this Book of Self Re-education

We shall tell you again and again
how to use this book of self re-education.
Please listen when we warn you
not to repeat the exercises
like gymnastics.

Once understood, exercises should only be *applied*
while doing ordinary daily movements.
Movements which must be done to perform
the necessary daily tasks.

To prepare or just eat a meal.
To dress, clean or arrange a cupboard.
Do not judge one occupation
more important than another.
Do not start to choose, to compare, to prefer.
Follow the plan of the day
according to the simple necessity of doing a thing
when it is due to be performed in the moment.

While acting, or speaking, your attention must apply a basic exercise.
For instance, execute the sloping spreading movement from the spine.
Or create the feeling of the two sides in the back of the body
in opposite directions.

Do not follow the movements of your acts.
Absorb very intensely the basic direction of the movement of the exercise
and stay conscious all the time of its support.
In this way when you "repeat" the exercise
it will never be the same,
as you apply the exercise
anew on every occasion.

The basic exercise keeps the body tuned
well-structured and functioning freely.
The ever-new relation of the basic exercise
to all the different acts you perform,
or the words you say,
will help you to avoid the dull mechanical reactions,
and morose atmosphere in life,
when you repeat over and over again
the same movements.

Please give your full attention,
and put the application of the exercise into practice.
Slowly change your habits in this way.
Discover what it means to live,
and begin to understand the meaning of life.

Remember that all Form is but Movement

Remember that all form is but movement,
and all variety of form but a variety of movement.
Still in each form alike works that *one* movement,
by which it is created in each moment
ever anew.

A movement of gathering – and form IS
a CENTRE.
And the tide of space is coming to
and going from this Infinite Centre,
is gathering and radiating
at the same time.

And all that is around a form
gives freely to the gathering movement of that form.
From its Centre given back, it radiates
and flows to all sides into space
to forms around it.

Thus is each form unique expression of all other form.
Each "I" is ALL, reflected through its gathering.
And in each form the Centre, infinite,
empty and full at the same time,
is that of Being all-pervading,
is that of Essence pure, divine,
outlaid in space, revealing by the movement of form
that which does not move, ever the same.

"Being Not-Being"

"Being Not-Being", forever one.
Inseparable, these two together.
Source of creation.

Essence of form "Being Not-Being",
Omnipresent, revealed in life.
Ever the same, still ever varied.
Never repeated, but fresh and new
in every form, in every moment.

And all pervading the universe.
Manifest in every single form
however small.
This simple truth brings life eternal
to every moment of each form existing.

"Being Not-Being", forever linked.
Nothing can be without Not-Being.

Who comes to be and not to be,
comes to perfection and to live
wholly and fully.

Death to him
becomes a state of life,
and mortal form has immortality
in this pure grace of understanding.

Part I

This is a letter to Dr. Jacques Donnars in Paris,
who was the first doctor to study with me
in order to heal himself,
and to treat his patients
on the basis of the teaching
of Space Functions in the human body.

One should know the structure and functions
of the human body.
One should know them well.

The whole body is functioning.
A coordinated functioning of all the organs.
They function according to their structure.

The human body is given us
as an expressive instrument.

Space is expressive Essence.
Space is creative Essence.
This Essence reveals itself
in all forms in the universe.
It manifests in the human body
through all the functions of the organs.
The revelation of this Essence
works in the human body
as the creative breath,
known by the term
Prana.
It is the structure and functioning of the organs
which gives us the clear knowledge of direction
when we are working in our inner space.

Directions are spatial expression.
Do not forget:
Space is the only Creative, Expressive Essence.

The exact clear knowledge we can obtain
about the structure, the organs and the functions in our form,
the absolute understanding of the build of our body
and all that moves inside our skin.
Knowledge we can note down,
teach and pass on to others,
knowledge about everything concerning our physical and measureable form.
This is the kind of knowledge we should obtain and perfect,
with the same clear consciousness and exactness
during the workings of the Creative Essence,
through all the substances of our bodily form.

How can we open our minds to this clear insight
of the relationship between Essence and Substance?
That is the question.
Through 70 years of research
we have sought the answer to this question.
And I think I have found the answer.

It is a heritage which my husband, my son, and I
would like to leave to other human beings.
To men and women who would be ready
to accept the inner discipline,
and the continuous process of application
of the knowledge born from inner research.

And ever anew apply it in all circumstances
and in all situations.
In order that they may learn to master
the workings of this Creative Essence
in the substances of their bodies.

These workings will manifest themselves
in attitudes and gestures, in facial expression,
in movements in outside space,
and in the intonation created by inner movement
in the sonorous gestures of the voice.

Only men and women choosing once and forever
to accomplish their destinies in this way,
can become in human evolution
new and perfect human beings.

It is for this purpose that we live on earth.
It is the message of our life.
Everyone of us may accomplish this.
For even the most humble are meant to fulfill
their task in the infinite harmony of creation.

To do wholly whatsoever one does,
with that inborn taste of love and of perfection,
which is sometimes hidden, buried,
driven away from our awareness,
but stays rooted in the very depth of our being.

This will set us free forever from the choice
between good and evil.

For good is not perfection.
To do good can make us proud.
And pride feeds evil.

Evil can sometimes lead straight
to consciousness of perfection.

To fulfil wholly and fully the humblest task.
This is simple,
perhaps not easy.
It may not bring us that special happiness
we keep on looking for in vain.
But it may bring us peace and serenity,
and help us to create joy
in those around us.

Let Us Begin to State Precisely

Let us begin to state precisely,
how we can start to have a clear consciousness
of the infinite, formless and measureless
Essence of Space.
And how we can obtain the exact knowledge
about its workings.
Let us learn to partake
in its creative process of expression.

First let us realize that space
even in a thimble is infinite.
Space is Essence in all things,
in all limited forms
small or big.

Lao Tsu has taught this
six hundred years before Christ's birth.
And Chuang Tsu, the great poet, his adept
wrote it down.
And so we have the "Tao Te Ching"
that noble book.
It says in simple terms,
that with clay and a wheel
we can create a cup.
But the essence of the cup
is the space within the cup.
The reason for creating it –
to hold a liquid.
And so it is with four walls and a roof –
a house,
but meant within its space
to shelter people.

19

All this brings home to us,
to our knowledge and to our comprehension,
that Space is the Essence
in all form
without any exception.

We should give attention
to this essential working of Space
in our own form.

Our relationship to other forms
in Space around us,
is *direction*.

It is quite clear, that we can
not only know,
but we can choose and follow
and express,
all that we wish others to know,
by the directions of our movements
and our gestures.

And we can give attention
and understand,
what other people and other things
want to convey to us,
by the directions of their movements and their gestures.

The real sense of all form,
of its beginning, its existence and its life,
lies in that absolute at-onement
of Essence and Substance.

Know that Science tells us —
"Space is inherent in all movement."

The Attitude which should be Taken by the Pupils

The attitude which should be taken by the pupils
who wish to start on self re-education,
on the basis of the teaching given in this book,
is important.

When there is the wish to control by inner experience
the structure and functioning of the body,
this first chapter should help the approach to the exercises.
For we should feel and know by feeling,

what goes on inside our physical form.
The foreword contains not merely intellectual information.
It must not lead to statements
about abstract subjects.
It should not be read or talked about,
or passed on by repeating words.
All exercises will be movements,
movements of attention in space.

We must gently detach our attention
from where it wanders in outside space.
Then let it start to move
towards different regions inside the body,
to where we wish to feel by sensation,
the exact structure and functioning of these parts
we have chosen to explore.

When we detach, for instance,
our attention from some place in space in front of us,
to where our eyelids are,
we move on a trace through space
in a definite direction –
we approach our face.

When then this movement touches
the surface of our mask,
we can feel by sensation
where the eyelids are.
The eyelids may close.
We will be with and within our eyelids.

If we execute this exercise
and feel this trace we followed through space,
it may become the beginning
of a new consciousness of the direction
in which we move.

Soon we will be able
to undergo and know
the feeling of pure space-experience,
and become aware and able to master
direction as an expression of movement in space.

Every single exercise demands this preparation,
by which we at once create
the intimate relationship
between creative expressive Essence,
and the substances of our physical form.

It is a very different thing,
to focus hands, your own
or someone else's,
and state: I have a hand,
you have a hand.
Or,
to *feel* your hands and to be able
to do things with the hands,
fully alive in your feeling,
and fully present in the doing.

On the Advice of Pupils

On the advice of pupils we decided
to explain and teach in the foreword,
with great exactness,
one single exercise, as an example,
of how to prepare and execute
all other exercises.

Through what you have experienced
and learned already,
sensing and feeling the direction
in space of the movement,
you will reach the place in space
where you can feel and stay together
with those parts of your own body
you wish to know and to explore by sensation,
feeling them alive and at your disposition,
to help express whatsoever you wish to show
and to be understood by others.

So now we start again to prepare,
and to create the trace through space
and reach the eyelids.

Having arrived within, we are now going to learn
to feel the direction of their structure.
The fibres of the little muscles of the eyelids
are attached, left and right, to our nose-bridge,
and horizontally structured.
Straight they go in opposite directions,
from the nose-bridge to the outer corners of the eyelids
towards the temples.
It is in these same directions that they are renewed
by life's constant movement of renovation.

And the movement of their function
to shut and give our eyes repose,
performs itself by a movement in the same direction —
from the nose-bridge in opposite directions,
to left and right
to the outer corners of the lids.

Let us recapitulate, and state again.
We have learned to master first of all
the creation of an infinite relationship
with all the different parts of your own body.
Secondly, there where these parts in you
are present and alive,
you will be able to sense their structure.
And the directions of their structure
will enable you to feel the directions of their functions
according to their structure.
Then you will discover that these directions
of the structure and the functions
are co-ordinated with life's movement of renovation.
So, if your movements of expression
are in harmony with these fundamental movements of life,
of structure and of function in the same direction,
your movements will be fully alive,
spontaneous and creative.

Now we give you different exercises
you may start to execute,
and you will after the preparation
according to the indications given in the foreword,
be able, not only to feel and know
about the structure and the functioning
of the different parts of your body,
but also start to feel and know
the directions of that constant movement of renewal
of all the substances in your physical form.

This movement of renewal in our body
is life's creative activity,
which from the source of life in our form,
our centre of balance, the centre of gravity,
works in us this constant renovation
through all the substances of our organs,
bones, articulations, muscles and nerves.
So, we must by the exercises
free the body from all inner and physical contractions.

Our form is totally receptive.
And we should keep it
wide-open to all sides,

23

as we are told to do
by the oldest teaching written down
in the Holy Scriptures of the Vedas:
"Be not one-sided, be to all sides."

We ask you now
while you are sensing the structure and functioning
of the eyelids,
to try to state the feeling of the sensation
created in your inner space
just behind these lids.

A smile is born behind the eyelids,
caused by the sensation
of liberation of the eyelids,
from the strain and stress
when you often move them
forcibly downwards,
or pull them
towards the nose-bridge.

Try to execute these wrong movements,
and feel the entirely different sensations
they cause behind the lids.
And then again allow the eyelids
to perform the movement of closing
according to their natural structure.

Do the exercise
again and again,
each time making
a new approach on the same tracks,
and sense what and how you feel
in inner space.
And then be open to discover
and enjoy the feeling of liberation.
Then you can free yourself from stress
caused by contractions of the eyelids.

Open your attention then still more.
Awake, feel and become aware
that in your brain the exercise of the eyelids
has created a feeling of relaxation;
a tendency to let go
the constant strain of thinking
mechanically around and about
some bits of undigested thought.

I am sure you understand
that we are teaching you
to develop the function of attention,
intensifying its receptivity
which is *total*.

We are alas, always keen
to know and control everything
intellectually.

Let us do the exercise of the eyelids once more.
Then when we feel the brain relaxed,
let us open our attention still a little more.
And from the nose-bridge sense,
and feel, that the wings of our nose
have spread.
You did not do this spreading.
It did itself.
This discovery is important:
a liberating movement, which does itself
because of your having liberated
the single function of the eyelids.

Feel how below the spreading wings of the nose,
your breathing has become
one single movement.
And now you are totally liberated
from the wrong forced way of breathing:
of *taking* a breath,
and *pushing* it out,
which causes the impossibility
of moving and speaking
creatively, naturally, spontaneously.

Do not Repeat Exercises

Do not repeat exercises.
Recreate the sensation and the experience of an exercise.
It will lead you to many inner discoveries
of things very important for you to know.

Do not try to find out and invent things
of which perhaps you will lose control,
trying to use them for your own benefit,
at the cost of what you feel to be 'other'.
Destroying forms in space outside around you,

which are meant to feed your own identity
in form and in being.

Because all that is 'other', which is around you,
is gathering by the senses in the centre of your form,
creating you –
as a unique aspect of what is 'other',
and meant to be emanated from that same centre
of the form you call "I".
Revealing that you are a member of the human race
ready to serve the evolution of human beings.

The Eyebrows

Approach once more your face,
and the place where your eyelids are.
Feel how from the bridge of the nose
they stretch away to left and right
in opposite directions.
Then feel the eyebrows above these lids.
Their curves above the eyes
also part from the nose-bridge in opposite directions
towards the temples.
You will feel all the more
the eyelids stretch to their outer corners.
And when the eyelids close,
let the eyeballs come to rest
in the outer corners of their sockets.

Then stay awhile behind the closed eyelids.
You are within yourself,
detached from outer space.
Stay there just a while,
just a few moments rapt in inner vision.
A smile is born.

We are Going to Teach You a New Exercise

We are going to teach you a new exercise
which is of the utmost importance.
This exercise must be kept alive as a base
for mastering all creative expression
in word and deed.

You will begin to open your attention
and absorb behind the lovely shells of your ears
the sounds you hear in outside space.

All primitive people, and all animals
listen behind their ears.
Sounds from outside space –
there are always noises in outside space –
make the inner skins of your tympanons vibrate.

Do not let yourself be distracted by these outside noises.
Let the vibrations run along the nervous threads,
which will carry the sounds through your centres of attention,
leaving there impressions.
Then through your motor centres,
towards the top of the atlas vertebra
on which your head finds the balance
for its entire weight.

Then you will begin to learn, to feel and know
inner listening.
If you have felt and lived
this inner happening,
you will discover that your eyes
by this happening, have spread by themselves
towards the outer corners of your eyelids.
A movement you have learned before,
which taught you not to look at outside things.
You will not *look*
you will *see.*
When you begin to listen towards within
you will understand the inner meaning of all sounds, words and movements.

If you no longer *look* but *see*,
not trying to grasp for outside sounds,
but listen towards within,
and create a deepening inner silence,
where you will begin to receive
the answer to your question:
"What must happen in this moment?"
Then the answer will perform itself in you.
You are ready then for a new attitude in life.
You may feel,
even in the busiest moments during the day,
the back of your head
tilting slightly in a backward direction.
Then you may feel you are being carried through the day
towards the moment that you will lie down
on your bed,
and your head will sink into the cushion.

27

And while you go on
fulfilling your tasks
which perform themselves in you,
you will be helped by this intense feeling
of opening and entering the state
of perfect relaxation,
and total receptivity
of soul, mind and body.

Sit Down and Lean against the Back of the Chair

Sit down and lean
against the back of the chair.
Feel how the seat gives you full support.
Feel the ground beneath your feet.

Let your head lean and find support
against the back of the chair,
and rest in a backward direction.

Against all these supports
for the head, for the body, for the feet,
let the weight of your body drop.
In your back it slides down to the seat.
And the weight of your legs and feet
slide down to the ground underneath your feet.
Your arms are sustained by the arms of the chair.

Thus sitting detach your attention from outside space.
Approach the mask of your face.
It may find the places where your eyelids *are*,
and arrive in inner space behind the eyelids.

Linger there a moment at-one with the eyelids.
Feel how the muscular fibres stretch away
from the bridge of the nose
in opposite directions to the outer corners of the eyes.

Open your attention to the eyebrows above your eyes.
Trace their curves towards the temples.
You may feel all the more
how the eyelids stretch
to the outer corners of their sockets.
The eyelids stretching, close by themselves.
Behind the closed eyelids, a smile is born.
You are within yourself, detached from outer space.

Stay awhile with the inner vision behind the lids,
and feel between the eyebrows the birth of a smile.

Then you can discover
that the nostrils have spread like wings.
Outgoing, incoming breaths
are balanced on the flow of time –
at-one.

When We Execute the Exercise of the Eyelids

When we execute the exercise of the eyelids,
and arrive within our inner space behind these lids,
we lose our sight, and undergo a sensation of "nothingness".
Because in inner space we do not see things
as we are accustomed to see them in space around us.

But when we decide to accept this new state,
and try to undergo this new impression,
we may begin to feel the essence of space.

In and through space we can move
in any direction we choose.
Just as we move in outside space,
so in our inner space we can consciously feel
a pure space movement.

Let us give all our attention to this feeling,
and often undergo it,
and get familiar with this experience.
We can then partake in its action.
We can develop feeling, and consciousness of direction,
and thus begin to master inner movement.

We should never try to grasp intellectually,
a substantial organ or part of our body
during this inner process of space-experience.
We should only discover its place in our inner space,
letting the centres of attention absorb its presence.
Let us never isolate a single particle
in the narrow bounds of our physical structure.
This structure is kept alive by the movements of its functions,
for our whole body is co-ordinated function.
So we can discover by and by
the wonderful totality of our body,
our expressive instrument.

The Living Hair

Above the eyelids and the eyebrows,
you can feel the forehead.
Around the forehead is the implant of the hair,
rounding to left and right towards the temples,
and behind the ears descending.
Then bending,
to meet again
in the middle of the lower border of the skull-base.
Low in the neck,
there is a dimple,
where the head rests on the spine.

The hair grows backwards over the skull,
then behind the ears descends
and falls over the back
in backward space.
Our living hair flows downwards
and links us to that backward space,
protecting our neck and back
in which we lean.
And in which the memories of our past experience
mount,
when we need the fruit of our experience
for expression.

Remember that in every moment,
we are but the outcome
of all we have lived before.
The exercise of the living hair, will awaken in you
the awareness of movements in backward direction.

First of all the movement
towards the centres of attention
to left and right low in the skull-base.
It will also strengthen in you the feeling of the support
for the head on the spine.

In the mask and in your head,
every particle tends and is directed
towards this support.

By awakening in the different parts
of your head and mask
the feeling for the relation to this support,
you can by and by also strengthen
a direct sensing of the centres of your attention
behind the lovely shells of your ears,
and of *their* relation to the support
of the whole head on the topmost vertebra of the spine.

Most of the Natural Functions of the Body

Most of the natural functions of the body
perform themselves without any of our wilful doing,
but we interfere, and do not let them take place naturally,
thereby causing all kinds of obstructions.
In order to awaken these functions,
when we take a meal of food and drink
we should take the habit of sitting down quietly.
Then awaken the function of creating saliva in our mouth,
and let this function go on before, during and after
bringing food into the mouth.
The function of swallowing starts
to perform itself naturally again.
Keeping the saliva functioning,
the food glides to the back of the mouth
and down into the throat by itself.

This second function happening by itself
against the atlas vertebra at the back of the mouth,
allows you to awaken a third natural function —
listening behind the ear-shells.

Be Careful in Practising Yoga

Be careful when you learn Yoga,
when reading in the Bhagavad-Gita
that you should direct your gaze to the tip of your nose.

First sit down.
Plant the spine
and the sacrum
on the seat of the chair.

The spine will grow like the stem of a flower.
On the topmost vertebra
rests the weight of the flower of the head.

Lean in your back,
and let your eyelids,

from the bridge of the nose
spread to left and right,
in opposite directions
towards the outer corners
of the eyes.
Then feel the eyebrows
traced above the eyelids,
from the same nosebone
spreading to the temples.

The eyes under the lids
are nearly closed.
You will discover
that the nose very gently
becomes apparent
to the inward-turned gaze.

The wings of the nose will then spread.
The air underneath the wings,
gently goes out and comes in
on the rhythm of inner life.

The gaze only faintly mirrors
the nose.
The nose is there!

Most Exercises are Meant to Create Within You . . .

Most exercises are meant to create within you the possibility
of developing in your centres of attention,
low in the skull-base, their capacity of opening,
in order to receive and absorb impressions.

Impressions coming from outside space by way of the senses,
touch the inner skins of the senses,
and run along the nervous threads
to reach the centres of attention.

The centres, at the same time absorb from space within
the awareness of inner experience.
And from the centre of gravity
inspiration, intuition, intentions and ideas
mount from the depth of our being to these centres.
These outer and inner impressions
lead to the necessity of expression and of communication
with the world around us in outside space.
This happening will create movements inside our body in different directions,

movements in which creative force is inherent,
caused by the workings of the pure essence of space.
These movements awake in the centre of attention
inner awareness of feeling,
and one starts to sense the organs
and the directions of their functions.

Thus we obtain the mastering of our expression,
because Creative Essence animates
the movements of our physical instrument,
the body.

The Rhythm of Life in the Relative World   I

We hope that you are now choosing
an exercise every day,
setting out in an already familiar direction,
and open to discover
the new day you are living,
which starts when you wake up
in the morning.

Man, has alas, mechanized,
structured, and fixed human society
in such a way,
that after eight hours of sleep,
he wakes,
as if during the night
he did not live,
but takes up his life
in the morning,
burdened with the worries and the problems
of the night before.
Whilst during the hours of sleep,
unconscious of the narrow limits
of personality,
and the functions free from wilful domination,
the presence of the life-force
is restoring balance.
Man has been upsetting
this balance
in his daily life,
during the hours of his being awake,
damaging the wonderful instrument
of the human body.

And spreading damage in the world around,
trying to make others believe,
and himself,
that he does all
for the better,
fooling others and himself.
Those who simply and humbly
start on self-investigation, and self re-education,
do the exercises to receive knowledge
through individual experience.

They start to create the pattern
of a unique, and individual life,
different from all other lives.
No imitation of anyone else's acts or ideas,
not even of a Guru.

They will develop
the possibility
of forming groups.
Centres of mutual understanding.
And everyone free,
not separated
in the terrible way,
we in life
stay separated,
even from those who are most dear to us,
yet in our inner being so deeply longing
for at-onement.

The Rhythm of Life in the Relative World   II

After the night's rest
there is a wave of energy
spreading through the form,
through the body.
And the crest
of that wave bends
forwards-downwards,
towards noon.

Then the body needs a rest
and food.
A restful meal.
This is important,
as you will need a second wave
coming ashore,

to carry you
through the afternoon,
enabling
more spontaneous expression,
in another mode.

Respect these natural conditions
when you are planning
your day.

Towards the evening,
your psychic functions wake
more and more.
Do not forget
that the atmosphere changes during the day
and through the night.

Thus the theatre is open to human beings in the evening,
when the physical exertion in man ebbs.
Then the necessity for psychic food awakes.

Therefore the performers must be prepared and ready,
to lead the audience on the path
of creative experience.

The public inclined to repose,
and therefore open to receive,
will spontaneously open mind and body,
and spread and lean in their back.
They will not look,
they will *see*!

When the Veil of Sleep is Lifting

When the veil of sleep is lifting
in the early morning,
my eyes stay shut.
I am lying on my back.
Slowly I become aware
that my eyes behind their lids
have spread to their outer corners.
It feels as if my eyes had reached
my temples, like the eyes
on the Egyptian hieroglyphs,
and on Persian and Indian miniatures.
As vague noises from outside space
start to set my tympanons vibrating,

this feeling joins in the awareness
of the deep inner silence of sleep,
and the feeling of the eyes resting at the sides of my temples.
This awakes listening towards within
behind the shells of both my ears.

The awareness of the inner unity
of insight and this listening towards within,
joins then the sensation
at the back of my head,
sinking in the cushion.

It all creates a wonderful state
of just being alive
under the veil of sleep
and awakening to a new day,
to be and live, and let life express
through my being,
what must be done, and said, and sung
in the chorus of all forms in space.
The music of the spheres.

Part II

The Diaphragm   I: Phrenos

The diaphragm was
in the classic Greek civilization
called "phrenos".

The Term "phrenos" originally meant:
the unity of all the possibilities
of man's psychic expression.

Thus it is clear: the ancient Greeks knew
how the psychic tensions
within our bodies
can reveal, and can translate themselves,
by the physical tensions of this muscle.

And in fact: we found
that all emotional and spiritual expressions
in order to manifest,
depend upon three basic tensions
in the borders of this central muscle – the diaphragm.

The Diaphragm   II

The diaphragm is the central muscle of the human body.
This muscle is the mediator between the pelvis and the thorax.
The diaphragm has many very important functions.
Its structure is a work of art.
Its formation could be compared to the structure of the tongue.
It has like the tongue, a strong root
supported in the back by the lower back ribs.
Its muscular body, from the roots,
advances like the tongue in a forward direction.

Our tongue in our mouth is perfectly free,
but the outer borders of the muscular body of the diaphragm
start from where the back ribs begin to round off.
These borders of the diaphragm are here and there attached
to these rounded-off ribs,
to where the ribs start to mount
up to the front part of the thorax,
towards the breast-bone.

The function of these borders is to give massage
to the organs in the pelvis.
The movement of this massage,

39

presses in a backward-forward direction:
at the right-side on the liver,
at the left-side on the spleen.

The front part of the diaphragm is free.
It embraces the stomach,
giving this organ massage by pushing it gently
downward-backwards towards the spine.
The bowels underneath the liver, spleen and stomach,
are by the movement of massage
also moved downwards.
Thus in the pelvis, all the organs
are co-ordinated by this wonderful movement of massage.

The rhythm of this movement is changing constantly,
as the diaphragm swings
performing another function:
translating our psychic tensions into physical tensions,
in order that all we wish and must express
may become visible in our movements,
and audible in the intonation of our voice.

Let us now give special attention
to the frontal part of the muscle
embracing the stomach.
Breathing out, it makes the stomach descend
and approach the spine, in a backward direction.
By this movement of massage the air is drawn
into the lungs and expelled.

To enable the free part of the diaphragm to move
the stomach downwards-backwards,
the side-ribs must stay open while breathing out.
So breathing out, these ribs do not change
their open attitude and position.

When you let the ribs stay open
while the breath goes out,
and do not contract the outer borders of the diaphragm,
the air will be drawn in,
and you will have learned:
natural breathing.

We must give much attention
to keeping the diaphragm free
from the imposed contractions
of wilful, artificial breathing,
or by wrong application of yoga-exercises,
so often misunderstood
by adepts, and even by masters.

Natural Breathing   I

For natural breathing, we must not forget
that the frontal part of the diaphragm
stays free.

Natural breathing creates
a stomach-pit.
When breathing out,
the frontal part of this muscle
covering the stomach,
slowly retreats towards the spine.

The air flows gently in
under the spreading nose-wings,
glides backwards over the hard palate,
over the soft palate,
till deep in the mouth.
It then descends and spreads
against the backwall of the thoat,
and descending more downward in the windpipe,
passes between the vocal chords,
to left and right in opposite directions.

It passes also in the trunk, to left and right
beneath the shoulders,
into the bronchial tubes
and lower down into the lungs.

The air finds its support there
against the lower back and side-ribs.
Thus leaving the space beneath the breastbone free
beneath the frontal part of the central muscle
covering the stomach.
And the frontal part of the whole body
stays wide open and at rest.

We should always remember
that flowing out,
the air finds support in the bottom
of the pelvis,
and underneath the outer borders of the lungs.
The upper-front part of the whole thorax
and the mouth
stay absolutely free,
without any concern about
breathing in the air.

Natural Breathing   II

Practising natural breathing,
apply first the Prana-breathing
through the limbs.
Feeling where and how,
the upper armbones and the thighbones
have heads in their sockets.

Feel them in their right direction
to left and right:
the arms coming out of their cavities
underneath the shoulders,
and the heads and necks of the thighbones
coming out of their cavities deep in the pelvis,
point downwards right and left,
from these sockets.

Let your attention open once more
to the inside of your back,
to the region of the lower back-ribs,
then let a movement spread
to left and right in that region.

By this spreading movement,
the two outer borders of the muscle of the diaphragm,
just beneath the lungs,
will draw in the air.
This air finds support against the back-ribs,
and against the sides of these same ribs
where they start rounding off
in a forward direction.

Let your breath flow out evenly.
The coming-in and going-out of breath
will then become united in *one* movement,
like the movement of the waves of the ocean.

Your breath will support
all sonorous expressions
on an inner rhythm,
and also support all your movements.

The Quality of Natural Lung-Breathing

The breath flowing out
bears activity in expression.
A basic and most important thing to know.
Breathing out,
the air carries our activity.

Whenever you wish to act,
or to express yourself in speech,
perform your actions
on the out-going breath,
without pushing or squeezing
the air out.

It is sufficient to let your actions and words
be carried on the out-going breath.
We have only to feel and to be conscious,
that the human breath is
in itself a force.
Never *take* a breath,
nor hold it while you act.
Breath is a gift
which we should humbly accept.

As soon as you have spent the breath
and acted,
let the air enter into your lungs
while you stay relaxed.
Let the incoming breath be a gift.
It is a gift for your next activity.

Sometimes people wish to relax
and let go their breath.
They feel and think
that breathing-out is in itself a relaxation.
But that does not yet create
that state of total rest and freedom
we wish to attain.
Breathing-out in order to become relaxed
is a tremendous active search.

The gift of air
that enters into your lungs,
after quite naturally breathing out,
is the work of the outer-borders
of the diaphragm, through sucking in the air
and giving massage to the liver and the spleen.

You remember: these outer-borders
give massage to the organs in the pelvis,
and at the same time
draw in the air deep into the lungs.

Note that the movement of breathing-in
performs itself in very little time.
You may think
you only receive a small quantity of air.
Still it is sufficient!
Allow it to happen,
and give all your attention,
while the air comes in,
to what you wish to express.

We are in the habit of consciously
taking in as much air
as we possibly can.
We start to suffer
from pressure on the vocal chords,
and in the throat.
We try to master our breath in this way,
which proves to be and is
impossible.

Once More Natural Breathing

Many institutes announce special methods
of stomach-breathing, chest-breathing,
or teach the expanding of the side-ribs when inhaling,
and pulling them inwards when breathing out.

All these methods ignore natural breathing
according to the structure and functioning of the organs.
So the diaphragm takes to artificial breathing.
This causes serious degeneration
of many organs in our trunk:
a wrong co-ordination of the functions of the bowels,
of stomach, of heart and of lungs.
Thus blocking the natural co-ordination between trunk and head,
thereby upsetting the direct connection and balance
between the functions absorbing impressions,
and the creative process of expression.

Let us not continue to disturb our natural breathing,
but let this function take place deep in the pelvis,
sucking in the air by the lower borders of the diaphragm
where they give massage to liver and spleen.

44

This movement seeks physical support deep down
in the pelvis, against the big vertebra above the coccyx.

Then in us the storehouse of past experience will open.
Inspiration during inhaling
then spreads, mounts and creates,
according to the necessity of the moment,
the right word, the simple perfect act
due to be expressed in just that moment.

And at the same time, the same movement
descends through both legs
towards the earth.
The whole form is then supported
in perfect balance.

This physical support in the bottom of the pelvis
is there at-one with the psychic support.
Only when at-onement
of the physical and psychic support is not disturbed,
the thorax stays relaxed,
and the lungs free from strain and stress
let the breath carry the sound
of its spontaneous intonation in word and song.
It will then carry all your movements
in a natural way.

We Start Once More to Spread Our Eyelids, Eyebrows and Nose-Wings

We start once more to spread our eyelids, eyebrows and nose-wings,
and feel how the lobes of our brain relax,
and how from the implant of our hair around our forehead,
the hair covers our head in a backward-downward direction.

Then we open the centres of our attention
to where our lower backribs round off and become side-ribs,
and we plant the lower side-ribs
firmly on the back-side of our hip-bones.
The side-ribs then widen, and we can lean backwards in the waist
against the roots of the diaphragm.

Breathing out the stomach descends
in a backward direction towards the coccyx,
by the movement of massage
the diaphragm gives to this organ.
The centres of our attention absorb this descending movement
and the new condition inside our pelvis.

We then calmly await the necessity of the gift of breath.
We receive this gift, leaving our stomach low
as we must not grasp at a gift.
On the given support of the lower ribs on the hip-bones
the borders of our diaphragm, start in the rounded-off ribs
to give massage to the liver and the spleen,
by a movement in a backward-forward direction.
Then again the free part of the diaphragm
will continue the massage of the stomach.

So we become aware that the one movement of massage,
that the diaphragm gives to all organs in the pelvis,
restores the unity of the movement of our breath:
in and out at-one.
Our lung-breathing and the breathing of our skin
are then co-ordinated
and carried by the breath of life,
the basic function of the centre of gravity.

The Greek name of the diaphragm "phrenos",
was given to this muscle,
as "phrenos" was the ancient term
for all man's psychic capacities.
The ancient Greeks knew that the tension of our psychic capacities,
was translated by the diaphragm into physical tensions.
Thus we can express ourselves spontaneously in the language of movement,
in perfect unison with the sonorous gestures of singing and speech.

The Function of Skin-Breathing

A very important function
starts in us from the moment
of our birth,
when we start to live in outside space.
It is the breathing of our skin.
This skin-breathing is very intense
for many years.
It is necessary to keep the skin of the babies clean,
as the pores must open
to allow this skin-breathing
to function intensely.
It is as necessary
as the breathing of our lungs.

In some parts of the body
the skin breathes in the air,
while in other parts
the skin expels the air —
even liquids,
as in perspiration.

46

Prana Breathing

Prana breathing is the breath of life —
simultaneous concentration-radiation,
the basic function of the centre of gravity.
It is the creative breath of space
inherent in all movements.
Each single movement being created by the three "Gunas".

We should not try to learn to master Prana breathing.
Breath is a gift.
Prana breathing is the gift of life,
creating our form, our living body.
It is sustaining all movements,
all functions,
renewing all substances,
and passing through every particle of the body.

We should receive the gift humbly
and become consciously aware of its working.
This we should learn
and we will tell you how.
It is important for many reasons throughout your life.
At the end of life it is this movement
which will carry us from this life through death
into the life after death.
Still the movement goes on
freeing our lifeless body from all physical substances,
which served us through our life on earth.

Relax and become aware
of the outflowing of breath.
Our centres of attention will become conscious of this happening.
Feel the stomach descend in a backward-downward direction
towards the "plane" of support
above the coccyx,
on which all movements find their basic support.
As we stay relaxed and keep the stomach as low as possible,
we should wait for the gift of breath,
not letting the stomach mount
nor grabbing for breath.

You did not notice that after breathing out
the outer borders of the diaphragm
begin to massage the organs in the pelvis:
the spleen, liver, stomach and the bowels.
This takes place in its own discreet way.
You are accustomed, and were taught
to take a breath.

47

This makes you self-willed,
not aware of another precious gift of support,
the earth.

You have not consciously accepted this gift
and without it you can achieve nothing.
How can we make this tremendous change of attitude,
and become aware of "doing not-doing"?
What is the outcome of keeping the stomach downward
as we await the gift of breath?
The diaphragm used to taking the breath in
through nose and mouth,
may mount rapidly causing a choking feeling.
Let the diaphragm jump.
Wait awhile,
and let us try to understand exactly
what made the diaphragm jump
and suddenly refuse to perform its movement of massage
which causes "natural" lung breathing, without our interference.
This movement being so gentle,
we are not even aware of the gift of breath.

A simple movement will and must take place.
The floating ribs will descend towards the back of our hip-bones.
In this way the sweet breath of Prana
will permeate our being.

The Co-ordination of Prana-Breathing

In the centre of the physical plane of support above the coccyx,
on which all movements find their support,
also the movements of lung and skin breathing,
the centre of gravity is situated.

In the centre of this "plane",
the movement of radiation-concentration of Infinite Essence,
inherent in all movement,
carries our movements by this creative breath,
Prana breathing.
Prana breathing radiates directly through our whole form into space,
through all the substances of the body.
The basic function of the centre of gravity
creates in us emanation,
and dynamic vibrations, giving a lasting moving quality
to our attitudes and facial expression.

If we try to let this basic "plane" of support,
the most important of the thirty-three supports in our back
mirror itself in the centres of attention,
it will not only awaken in our awareness
where it is located in our body,
but also, we will be aware of its function of concentration-radiation.
Its creative breath will enliven every particle in our body
on the flow of inner time.
Thus consciousness of rhythm is born in us.

Stretching and Yawning

Right at the beginning of our self re-education,
we should open our attention to the natural movement
of stretching.
So please follow and feel the sensation
of this movement.

The stretching movement starts
from the centre of gravity.
It starts just before the big vertebra
at the bottom of the spine,
from where the coccyx descends.

When you wake in the morning to a new day,
stay awhile in bed and lie on your back.
Then provoke stretching.
Feel how your sacrum begins to press downwards
into the mattress.
And how all your transversal abdominal muscles stretch
sideways to left and right.
The front part of the pelvis flattens.

Stretching is a yawning movement
in the pelvis;
spreading like the yawning movement in the throat,
to all sides.

From the middle of the lower border of the pelvis,
it stretches behind the necks and heads
of our thighbones.
And then the movement goes downwards
and reaches the outsides of the feet,
touching the earth;
finding there the remarkably small supports
for the weight of the whole body.

The stretching movement also goes upward
from behind the necks and the heads of our thighbones
through both sides of our trunk,
and stretches the arms out of the armpits.
Every time the involuntary movement of stretching and of yawning —
you may sometimes provoke it —
urges you to give in to it, and relax,
open your attention,
and undergo these movements intensely.
Control how it spreads through your whole body.
These natural movements are meant
to spread through the whole body,
supporting the movement of renovation.
That you may feel, and by feeling know
how life's renovating movement creates you in every moment,
and brings physical substances
to renovation.

On these basic natural movements
we have built our teaching.

When doing this exercise, whenever you can,
feel and help your four limbs
to stretch out of their sockets.
Always give full attention
when you stretch and yawn.
And *sense* and *feel* this natural movement.
It is nature which teaches you.
And let us hope that you will learn
in this natural way,
how you are structured
and how your form functions.

When we have taken the habit
of sensing through the whole body
the movement of stretching,
we should undergo this movement
and let it work.
We must keep our attention open
and start to know by feeling
how it works.
You must still ask from your attention,
not to make the movement of stretching yourself,
but to let the movement happen.
Abstain from every tendency
to spend your own activity
in doing the movement.

This is an important thing to learn.
Perhaps the most important.

Stop being a busy-body,
greedy to investigate
in order to control your acts.
Exploring is opening the centres of attention
to follow and feel
what goes on inside your body.

We are now going to apply this.
We will discover that we sometimes yawn
without stretching.
The movement of yawning takes place itself.
This has a very important consequence.

While yawning the throat opens wide.
You can feel the liberating movement to left and right,
inside the throat,
taking firm support on the throat-wall
behind the mouth.

While we yawn we should sense and feel
where exactly is the backwall of our throat,
behind the mouth and uvula.
There we should create a very intense
and ever-present consciousness
of this support for our voice,
on which the sonorous value in the throat
changes direction and enters into the mouth,
helping to create the consonants we need,
in order to express our inner feelings in words
before these words pass our lips,
the outer doors of our mouth.
For, if ever you decide to try
to master your emotional reactions,
you will then be able by this movement
to protect mind, soul and body
from damage caused by emotional disturbances.
Because lower down, the movement of yawning
will cause the inner organs,
of the stomach and the heart to descend.
The diaphragm and the bowels will retreat
going downwards in the direction of the spine,
to the backside of the body.

Try to undergo this movement of retreating backwards,
while the organs descend,
and open your attention,
follow and sense these directions.
Emotions suddenly,
sometimes with tremendous impetus,
lift the bowels and the stomach,

the diaphragm and the heart,
pass through the throat contracting
and mount into the brain,
creating a whirl of fragments of thought.
This happens,
because we have been educated
to ask the intellect
to help us
according to a fixed code
of reaction and behaviour.
You will ask the *intellect*
to tell you *how* to react.

This manner of reaction
will be the beginning of endless strife,
muddle and entanglement.
If you re-educate yourself
keeping the organs down and backwards,
and from the centres of attention
in the lower borders of the skull-base,
you descend along the spine
at the backside of your body,
you will find in your back
the support for whatever you must fulfil
in the given emotional dilemma.

When You Yawn First Wide then Deep

When you yawn, first wide then deep,
you will feel that you have a chin,
which is a cradle for your tongue,
offering the tongue a bed to rest in,
and to relax.
Then you will find support for one of your most important tasks,
to create consonants to join the vowels on the backwall of the throat.
This movement will be carried on the outgoing breath,
unhindered underneath the palate through the mouth
towards, and into outside space.

The tongue lying on its back in the cradle of the mouth,
finds then a firm support
for the broad front part of the muscle,
mounting against the lower teeth.
Then staying on this support,
the middle very relaxed part of the muscle
being at rest in the bottom of the cradle,

begins to play against the upper teeth
creating the different consonants.
These bounce against the backwall of the throat,
joining the vowels on their way into outside space,
threading words and sentences on the flow of time,
revealing on an inner dynamic rhythm
the meaning of the inmost expressive life of the words.

Stretching Once More

Let us once more practise stretching.
I, myself very often come back to this movement.
It links us directly to the inner teaching
given to all living creatures.
It is the basic movement, nature and life create in us,
and we should let our attention feel what is being given to us.

To do this exercise
does not ask much of our time.
Waking in the morning
we just stay a few moments longer in bed.
Lying on our backs
we can then lazily provoke stretching.

But we must be very attentive
to how this movement of stretching starts;
from the centre of gravity
deep in the pelvis
just in front of the last big vertebra,
in the lower border of the spine
from where the coccyx starts.

We then shall feel how the sacrum
is pushed backwards into the mattress.
How at the same time, there is a strong push
from the same centre left and right,
passing at the back of the heads of our thighbones.

From there the movement runs
through our legs downwards
into the feet.
At the same time the movement runs upwards stretching
along both sides of our trunk,
and pushes the arms out of their sockets.

Further upwards in the neck,
and in the throat,

we feel how
against the backwall of our open throat,
the movement restarts with great force
and makes us yawn.
From this backwall in the throat
it starts through the whole head.
We can feel the roots of our hair,
and how the hair begins to grow on our skullbone.

The feeling of yawning in the throat
can make us realize,
that starting to stretch
down in the pelvis,
we feel
as if from the centre of gravity
we were yawning,
and as if this yawning movement
were spreading through our whole body.

We should let the feeling of this stretching movement
impress us very deeply.
We should be intensely attentive to this feeling.
We can then realize,
how we have grown
by a similar movement,
(which followed exactly the same way through our body)
through so many years
from babes until we became adults.

As this movement from the centre
opens the whole body to all sides,
it makes us aware
that we are totally receptive.
We will *feel* this receptivity,
which will keep all our functions
free from contraction,
and fully capable of functioning naturally,
freely, lightly.
So we will stay healthy in body,
in mind and in being.

The Little Town

We are going to teach you through your creative imagination
about the nervous system, and the bones and muscles
in the backside of your body.
We are going to create the awareness and feeling
that these parts of your body
are squares, streets and lanes
of a small town.

We descend in this small town
underneath the border of the skullbone
by the lane in the neck,
descending along the whole length of the spine.
At the same time, also descending
in the two pairs of adjoining small lanes
of the motor centres and the centres of attention.
These two pairs, together with the lane of the spine
form a pathway of five straight lines
descending to the coccyx,
where in the middle of the coccyx,
at the very bottom
lies our centre of gravity,
the centre of balance of our form,
of our body, mind and soul.

These five lines manifest
in the substances of our back,
and reveal by space movements
the Presence of the Creator
in all the substances of the body.
These space movements move through the insides of the shoulder blades
next to the spine.
The shoulder blades are two squares in the small town.

From these squares, two lanes
lead through the tendons at the back of the armpits
and through the tricep muscles in the upper arms,
down to the elbow joints.
Then through the arms
underneath the wrist-joints,
along the outsides of the cup of our hands
and along the spreading fingers
into outside space.
From the squares of the shoulder blades,
two pairs of streets descend
along the outsides of the trunk of the body,
and link the squares of the shoulder blades

55

to two squares low down in the pelvis,
behind the necks and heads of the thighbones.
Then straight downwards
they descend in two lanes leading out of the small town,
downwards to the only outward support
of the earth,
through the outsides of the soles of our feet,
which touch the earth.

Movement of the Limbs   I

Man's activity all through life,
from the cradle to the grave,
finds expression in movements,
carrying him
from one place to another.

He moves according to his wishes,
to perform actions
here or there.

Walking, his legs must carry him.
Working, his arms must perform the acts.

It is evident therefore,
that man should learn to master
the movements of his limbs,
in order that he may learn to know
the structure and the functioning
of legs and arms.

Most people move about
with legs and arms decapitated.

They know
the upper-armbone has a head
at the top of the bone.
The head of the armbone
belongs to the arm.
The head being bigger
than the body of the bone
fits into a cavity,
a socket inside the thorax.

The head of the armbone
inside this cavity
underneath the shoulders,
forms an articulation.

Arm-movements start inside these sockets,
from behind the heads of the armbones.

These movements take their support
inside these cavities,
at the back of the heads of the armbones
against the shoulder blades.
The arm-movements always start
out of the sockets,
and then downwards
through the whole length of the arm,
through elbows, wrists and fingers.

All movements start on a support.
While we move
we should always be
conscious of this support.
From the supports, we can feel
the *direction* of the movements.

The expressive value in movement,
can only be felt
by the *consciousness of direction*.

This consciousness can only be experienced
from where a movement starts from its support.
Only then can we have this consciousness
and feeling of direction.

Before practising this exercise
for legs and arms,
it is very beneficial
to practise the former exercise of stretching.
Stretching is
an inner natural impulse,
pushing the heads of the thighbones and armbones
out of their sockets.

The heads of the thighbones are differently set,
not like the heads of our armbones.

In front of the cavities in the pelvis,
the necks and the heads of our thighbones
enter these sockets,
from left and right,
and dive deep inside these cavities.
But the heads of the thighbones
belong to our legs.

It is *behind* these heads,
that our advancing movement in walking
starts, and finds support
against the sacrum and the backbones in the pelvis.

While walking our legs
move in alternation
left and right,
in a balancing movement,
on an inner rhythm,
which when felt and accepted
creates a wonderful consciousness
of being carried through space,
as on wings.

Do not forget that all arm-movements
are carried and supported
by the legs.
And thereby move in the same rhythm,
in wonderful co-ordination
with the movements of the legs.

When this is felt and absorbed,
by the deep consciousness of movement
present in our form,
a dancing quality awakes
in the whole body.

How happy we could be
if this were understood
and taught,
as it was by the ancient Greeks.
We sometimes proudly say
that we have built our culture
on their civilization.
Were it but true!

Still it is open to all human beings
from East and West,
to learn to master the limbs.
We need only listen
inside our inner space,
and discover and feel
this inner rhythm
whenever we walk.

Movement of the Limbs   II

What happens when we move
with decapitated limbs,
losing consciousness of direction:
what happens, for instance, in the arms
and underneath the shoulders?

The shoulders will lift the weight of the arms,
suspend it for a while
then let it drop.
The movements of the arms will be mechanised.

All we wish to express
will then be uncreative.
Will be performed
by *wilful* lifting.

As for the legs it will be the same problem.
We will walk from our hips,
lift the straight part of our thighbones,
and so lose consciousness
of the natural movement,
and of the natural rhythm,
while walking.

In all our articulations
there is the passing and the play
of space-breathing.

This is not known nor understood,
and not practised in the West.
Lack of this knowledge,
because of the lack of *feeling* movements,
causes our movements to be mechanical.

"Why Must I have a Straight Back?"

Just like the sap in trees
before the tender season of the early spring
mounts in the stem and branches of the trees,
and creates a wonderfully coloured hue of gold and purple
around the network of the branches.
So mounts a movement
inside the spinal chord,
and all along the tendrils of the nerves.

And by this movement,
your wishes and ideas,
intentions, and intuitions
and memories
are mounting in your back
and carried to the brain;
where all the wonderful capacities remain
open to creative thought and images,
which will enable you to express
to all your fellow creatures
what you wish or need to know.
All that lives in your deepest consciousness
can mount from inner space
into the space around you.

Raden Ayou Jodjana wrote this poem to her godson, Roberto, aged eleven, in answer to his question:
"Why must I have a straight back?"

A New Series of Exercises:
"Spreading"

Let us from now on compose a series of exercises
from which you can choose each day,
and establish by and by a new consciousness of your living body,
freeing it from unnecessary constraint.
It will create in you beauty and attractiveness.

There is the movement of spreading.
Nature helps you there.
You know that nature causes in you the necessity of stretching and yawning.
You have only to open your attention each time you stretch and yawn.
You can even, if you wish, provoke this movement.
Then you will discover for instance,
that swimming, rowing, and many other occupations
demand the same basic exercise of stretching and yawning.

In order that this may happen easily,
without too much of your own doing
we are going to propose a further series of exercises.

"To Lean in the Back"

Lie down
and accept the support of the back.

Let your attention open towards downwards.
It will awaken
the feeling inside your spreading body
of how you touch the bed.

Feel the bed being there
beneath your back.
Then open your attention
still more downwards.
Let it absorb the floor
which supports the bed,
feeling very intensely the direction downwards.
Still more downwards
absorb and feel the presence of the earth.

You know that the earth is floating in space
carrying you and the bed.
Still more downwards
are heavens and stars.

So when you stand up
and walk on the earth,
feel and know that beneath you,
beneath the earth which you tread,
there are stars and heavens.

"To Sink"

You dive into yourself
to reach the source of life
to meet there the Presence.
The Presence creates you
ever anew
in every moment.

Still deeper, feel and know the earth,
and tell her with your feet
about yourself.

Then you will learn to dance,
and express with your whole body
what you feel, and how you are.

61

And the earth
she will answer.
She will tell you
wonderful things
about her love
for all the creatures
she carries and feeds.

So dive deep!

A Simple Basic Exercise: Spread, Lean, Sink

A simple basic exercise to learn to master inner movement,
built up on the Motto: Spread, Lean, Sink,
translating itself into visible expression in movement.

Lie down on your bed.
Let your back sink in the mattress.
Let your head rest in the cushion.
Slowly spread in your head and face.

Spread the arms out of the sockets.
Let them totally relax.
Spread also your legs out of their sockets.
Let your feet by their weight drop outwards.

Imagine that at both sides of your bed a friend is sitting.
The friend on the right side is sitting on the floor.
The friend on the left side is sitting on a chair reading.

Slowly open your attention from its centre
towards the friend sitting on the floor,
on the right-hand side of the bed.
Then your attention will make your head
slowly turn to the right on the cushion.
The weight of your body will then also
shift itself in your back towards the right side.
Your right arm and hand may move on the blanket
in the same direction, and intensify
your connection with the friend sitting on the floor.

Tell this friend softly that you will for a moment
speak to your friend sitting on the chair,
at the left side of the bed.
Addressing these words whispering to your friend at the right,
you do not detach your attention from this friend.
You only open from the support, on the right-hand side,
in the back of your head,
the centre of attention at the left side.

62

The opening of your attention towards the left will make your head,
turn slowly towards the left,
without detaching you from the friend at the right-hand side.
The whole right side of the body stays directed towards the right.
But the weight inside your body from the spine on
will begin to shift slowly from right to left.

All these movements will be very light,
and only brought about by that slow shifting of your attention,
from right to left in your totally relaxed body.
Always leaning backwards in the bed
the weight spreading
over the whole length of your body from top to toe.

In this way you can keep in contact
with your two friends.
You can without effort communicate with them
by subtle, gentle, light movements
from right to left, and from left to right.

N.B. The principle of this exercise
can be transposed into any attitude,
and be applied in sitting, standing position
and in walking.

The Motto

The Motto: spread, lean, sink,
presents three verbs, three movements.
These verbs and movements are connected,
with the three dimensions of our form.

We have already learned to excute
many exercises.
We know by feeling
what it is to spread in opposite directions,
to left and right.
We learned also to lean,
and find supports for forward movements
in the backside of the body.
And we gave attention,
looking for support
for our upper body
in a downward direction.
We let the weight sink
in the direction of the earth,

first spreading the weight
in the back, low down in our pelvis.
Then let the weight go on descending
along the outside of our legs and feet.

The three dimensions of our form
are not the actual measurements of our body.
They are the three basic proportions of life in our form.
These three dimensions are the basic expression of our being,
and give us the possibility of endless variation
in movements in our inside space
and in outside space around us.

Attention   I

To give attention.
It is the simplest and the purest
act of love.
The greatness, the joy, the rapture
and the beauty of all love,
depends on the intense receptivity
of our attention.

So open wide the whole body.
Receive the incoming tide of space.
Open the body from the centre.
So that your whole being can absorb
all that wishes to be felt and known by you,
with the full and silent comprehension
of love.

Become wholly receptive.

Love does not manifest itself by emotional upheaval
in the body and the mind.
Love is not sentimental.
Its expression is a natural response from within,
and can only come to life
when you let impressions
that enter by the doors of your senses
be received by your attention,
in the bottom of the cup of your skullbone.
Let these impressions descend
deep-down into your body
to the bottom of your spine.
To the bottom of the sacral bone,

where the in-flow of impressions
causing inner experience
will stir your life's Essence.

The Essence then starts to move,
You will be moved in the depth of your inner being.

If *you* are not moved,
how can you move others by your expression?

Only when you allow
the natural digestion
of the psychic food absorbed by the senses,
will there be no strain or stress
expressing in a natural way
what moves you, and what you feel.

Spontaneous expression will mount in the spine
upwards towards the centres of attention.
Then spread and awake all the intellectual capacities,
which wonderfully creative,
will partake in expression;
in acts, in words
vibrating with pure expressive essence.

So allow the impressions
to reach the centre of your being.

Attention   II

Now let us try to understand
what takes place underneath our skull;
and how the capacities of the intellect
should work together.

We mostly use our intellectual capacities
without discrimination.
They all have their abode
beneath the cortex,
the lining of the skull.
They work together in intimate relationship
though each of them works
according to its own structure.

Attention is the basic capacity of the intellect
we must consider, and start to educate.

Attention is receptive and absorbs
all that enters through the doors of our senses.

When we are born and enter into life, here in this world,
we do not yet think nor create images.
These two capacities of intellect stay dormant
beneath the infant's skull.

But our attention is wide awake
and linked to the lower part
of our brain,
which works instinctively
like the brain of animals,
and drives the infant on to seek
warmth and food.
Then we live on the senses of touch and taste.

We go on living by these instincts and sensations
without a thought,
even without knowing,
attached by love to our mother.
There is the direct consciousness of wellbeing
when we experience,
feel, touch, and taste,
and find warmth and food.
The sense of touch causes sensations
in infants by impressions.

Now listen well, and try to understand
and always remember:
touch is the first sense.
When coming into this world as an infant,
we learn important basic truths
through the direct knowledge and memory of movement.
These memories stay on and alive
in the substances of our body.

Attention   III

The gentle act of giving our full attention,
opens wide our mind into inner space.
In the body we feel a movement spreading to all sides,
creating more space within.
All that asks for attention
can enter and find a gentle home,
in the centres of attention.

66

Never focus your attention
on things or persons in outside space.
And do not intrude –
stating what is different in them,
finding fault with the difference.
Why should you interfere?
Why should they accept your fixed opinions,
how to think, or how to live?
If you let the impressions enter the centres of your attention
descending into your source of life,
insight and knowledge will come to you.
No one will be capable of understanding 'what is other',
who does not give attention,
does not perform that simple, gentle act.

The Presence does not create two forms alike!

Attention   IV

Most exercises are meant to create within you the possibility
of developing in your centres of attention
low in the skull-base, their capacity of opening
in order to *receive* and *absorb* impressions.

Impressions coming from outside space by way of the senses,
touch the inner skins of the senses,
and run along the nervous threads
to reach the centres of attention.

The centres at the same time, absorb from space within,
the awareness of inner experience.
And from the centre of gravity
inspiration, intuition, intentions and ideas,
mount from the depth of our being to these centres.
These outer and inner impressions,
lead to the *necessity* of expression and of communication
with the world around us in outside space,
creating movements inside our body in different directions;
movements in which creative force is inherent,
caused by the workings of the pure Essence of Space.
These movements awake in the centres of attention
inner awareness of feeling,
and one starts to sense the organs
and the directions of their functions.

Thus we obtain the mastering of our expression,
because Creative Essence animates
the movements of our physical instrument
the body.

The Centres of Attention   I

In this book we often mention
two centres of attention.
There is but *one organ*.
This centre has, however,
two sides.

One of these sides belongs
to the left side of the body and the brain,
finding its support through the whole left side of the body
down to the ground underneath the left heel.
The right side of the centre of attention
is directed towards the right,
and through the right side of the body
reaches the right heel
and the earth underneath.

The two centres of attention
are wholly receptive.
They absorb all the sensual impressions,
and pass them on in a downward direction
through the nervous system in our back
to the centre of gravity.
Thus the centres of attention
co-ordinated to the centre of gravity,
establishes our balance,
which creates in us the basic feeling
of symmetry.
The two halves of the body,
from the apex through the spine and legs,
descend in opposite directions towards the earth.

We should, however, be careful
not to separate the two halves,
by pushing them in opposite directions
in the skull-base, towards the cavities of the ears.

The two halves of the one centre *are there*,
awaiting the sound vibrations
entering the cavities of the ears to penetrate
and be absorbed, and passed on
to the centre of gravity.

We never should shift the two halves of our centre of attention
towards the cavities of the ear.
We should carefully safeguard
the unity of the organ,
but feel the symmetry of the two halves.

We should be careful not to contract the organ,
which would upset the basic feeling of symmetry
and natural balance in our form.
Therefore, we often remind you
of this basic state we should re-educate,
by mentioning the *two* centres of attention.

The Centres of Attention   II

The organ of our attention is situated inside the cerebellum,
in the border of the skull.
As we have told you,
it has two centres at the left and right side of the spinal chord.
Each side of the body has its own centre of attention.

The different centres of all muscular activity,
which allow us endless variations of movement
are also situated in the cerebellum.

Thus the infant learns by and by to stand on its feet
and then to walk,
without the brain telling it how to do this
through creating mental pictures of movements.
The body slowly and very deeply absorbs the processes
of learning to accomplish these movements,
and will keep a direct consciousness of these processes,
and remember all through life
how to accomplish these movements spontaneously,
without needing the command and control of the brain-cells.

All the centres of muscular activity in the cerebellum
allow the body to move "automatically", but
not like a machine.
The brain-cells underneath the skull totally relaxed,
mirror the movements.
We then will live conscious feeling of our movements,
and those around you will see you move,
will follow how your movements flow from their supports,
along the nervous chords in the direction of their fulfilment.

69

The Centres of Attention   III

First of all we must restore the total receptivity of the centres of attention.
When executing exercises do not fix mind-pictures of movement.
Do not let the mind impose these fixed schemes on the body,
and order the movements according to these pictures.
We must create in ourselves the interrogative state
before executing the exercises,
and breathe out whilst performing them.
Perform all movements on the outgoing breath.
They must always start from a support,
and then run along the threads of the nervous system.
From the consciousness of the supports,
feel the movements run along the threads
and awaken sensation and awareness of the direction of their tracks.
Feel and undergo movements on the flow of time.
This asks a deep understanding and an ultimate choice:
of changing our bad habits
from wilfully moving and using our attention to direct movement,
and so disturbing its receptive functions.

The consequence of this bad habit,
such as constructing and fixing mind-pictures of movements,
and creating aims we wish to reach,
kills the expressive value of the *directions* of the movements;
for we have already arrived somewhere in the future
before any movement has taken place.
In this way we never express
the birth and accomplishment of a movement in time.
We must become aware by sensing and realizing
the terrible deterioration, ruining the nervous system,
destroying balance and the rhythm of life.

Let us put the question, is there a remedy
which will stop this destructive process?
Let us ask ourselves whether balance and inner rhythm can be restored?
The answer is in the affirmative.
Yes, we can learn to become directly, naturally expressive,
but the desire must be there to achieve this.
Nothing can be done if we are too weak to choose,
to bring ourselves to the decision,
of starting on the only path leading to the liberation of stress,
and to positive results.

We Feel it would be Well to Give Attention Again

We feel it would be well, to give attention again
to the structure of the head and the brain,
and to the functions of its organs,
especially to the many different important functions in the brain-cells.
Firstly to the basic function of the centres of attention,
which spread around the topmost vertebra of the spine.
The top of this vertebra is the very small support
on which the full weight of the head rests;
and on which all movements of the head
and *all facial expressions* find support.

Some great masters from the East,
have warned the Western world,
that the wrong working of our mental capacities
will lead to disastrous effects.
Already, for a long time, great disturbance
has been caused in our mental capacities,
and has upset the balance of our psychic and physical behaviour.
In nature we have slowly destroyed
soil, air and water.
Thus we are extinguishing life on this planet.

Let us therefore give attention and absorb knowledge
about the simple perfect structure of our form,
of its organs, and their functions;
and free soul, mind, and body from the constant strain
by which we cause the terrible social conditions
in which we live;
destroying all life on this planet.

The brain covers and envelops those parts of the nervous system
which lie under the skull-cap, and behind the face in the lower part of the head.
Behind the backwall of the throat
there is only a thin layer of brain-cells.
In the middle of this layer is located
the basic organ of our intellectual capacity of attention.
Its two sides lie below the atlas-vertebra
on the top of the spine.

You know all this already,
but you should feel it,
and be able to retire and *stay*
in the organ of attention.
Only then you can establish
the intense and intimate relationship
of the centres of attention with the centre of gravity.

This poem is not a repetition of information,
it is a new introduction to knowledge
and the possibility of the application of this knowledge.
We beg you to obtain by daily work,
this intense and intimate relationship
between the centres of attention with the centre of gravity.
These centres together, absolutely united
can give you perfect balance of your human form –
the body at-one with all psychic and physical capacities of expression.

It also establishes the perfect unity and balance
between impressions and expressions.
Impressions are the food you need for expressing yourself.
You cannot express yourself in terms,
that are not already stored in your inner space,
in the space inside your body in the centre of gravity.

Since you took your first breath in this world,
impressions started to enter into that space,
and to gather an enormous amount of expressive possibilities
deep down in your body,
in your centre of gravity.
First of all by *movements* nature has taught you.
Much later by thought and speech.

II

The process of gathering impressions,
and the process of expression,
pass through the spine,
and through the nervous system in the back.
This is the reason that all inner supports are situated
in the back and the neck of the body.
Impressions *descend* and are stored
in the depth of our being,
and in the depth of our body
in the centre of gravity.
There they become our means of expression.
Expressions *mount* from there to the brain.
The brain-cells above the lower part of the face
lie above the eyebrows,
and above the nervous system of all the senses:
above the nerves of the eyes, ears, nose and mouth.

The brain-cells have membranes
which should stay totally relaxed and without any wrinkles.
These membranes have a mirroring quality,
and like a pure mirror undisturbed,

reflect all that touches their very sensitive surfaces.
They never grasp nor try to hold.

All our motor capacities are also situated in the back of the head
closely united to the centres of attention.
In the domain of these cells, lie the capacities
of imagination, of thought
and all the means which allow us to communicate with the outside world.

Therefore, let us work and learn to increase
the feeling of these sensitive surfaces
of these membranes of our brain-cells,
by keeping them wide and still,
while sensations entering by the senses
pass underneath these cells
and become the mirror of man's mind.

Tuning the Body   I

When tuning the body, we must give back
total receptivity to our physical structure.
In order to be able to start on this re-education
of our expressive instrument,
we must know on what basis, and by what means
we can obtain this result.

It is absolutely necessary, that we first of all begin
to re-educate and develop our capacity of attention.
We have taken the wrong habit, when giving attention –
in order to gain knowledge,
both inside and outside ourselves –
of moving the organ of attention in different directions.

Most of us do not know where the organ of attention is situated,
and how it is structured.
This is the reason we cannot master its functions.
We push and move our attention about,
and thereby cause great damage to the organ,
and silence all the wonderful creative capacities in the brain.
We frustrate the wonderfully creative intellectual capacities
of an infant's brain,
and its natural evolution in becoming a true human being,
perfecting human qualities.

Let us try to listen to the necessary "in-struc-tions",
about this precious gift innate in us –
the ability "to give attention".

73

It is precise to say, that we should *open* our attention
because this is its real function.
We should know where it is situated:
low in the skull-base, in the middle of the border of the skull-bone,
where the head finds support on the topmost vertebra of our spine.
The organ of attention enfolds our spinal chord,
and it belongs to the back part of our body.
It has two centres,
one centre above the whole left side of our body,
the other centre above the right side.
In the same back part of our head are situated
all the motor capacities of our body.

The function of the centre of attention is to open,
to receive impressions, to mirror, absorb, and assimilate
all that enters through the doors of our senses
into our inner space,
as well as mirroring all that goes on in inside space.
By this mirroring quality of the centres of attention,
the organ passes all it absorbs
downwards in the backside of our body
to the centre of balance in the body,
the centre of gravity.
All the impressions that the centres of our attention receive,
travel down to the centre of balance,
in a place low down in the pelvis
in front of the border of the sacrum.
Descending, the impressions move through the abdominal organs.
We call what then happens in us – experience –
because by these abdominal movements, we are moved.
Deep psychic impressions are stirred.
They become visible in our attitude, and facial expressions.
They spread into outside space by our emanation.
Our capacity for expression is born,
it all becomes visible in space around us.
It makes our bodies move in gestures,
changes of attitude, and in movements of the whole body.
All these processes work in our inner space,
and are sustained and supported by space workings;
workings of Creative Expressive Essence
in all the substances of the physical form.

These space workings are functions of the centre of balance,
from where they pass to all sides through the nervous system.
They cause the expressions in movements of the body,
and in the intonation of our sonorous gestures –
in laughing, cheering, crying, sighing,
in exclamation, and in song and speech.

Tuning the Body   II

When we have attained the total receptivity
of the functioning of the organ of attention,
we will let sensations, feelings and experiences
directly communicate themselves
to the open mirroring and absorbing action of these centres of attention.

The centres never move.
They stay surrounding the support of the topmost vertebra of the spine.
While absorbing, they awake in us sensations, feelings, and experience that we undergo.
Thus we obtain knowledge about our form,
about all the parts of the body, of its organs and their functions,
of the totality of the body,
and of the coordination of all its parts.

The whole body will then become receptive,
and we will be attentive in every moment.
Thus we start to live each moment with full attention.

As life urges us to express ourselves, and to move,
intentions and impulses mount from the treasure house of past experience,
and we will know immediately what must be done *in the moment.*
All we do and say will then take place, and manifest in perfect harmony.
We will be linked to all outside forms,
to persons, animals and plants
even to all tools and objects that we touch.

Consciousness of Expression

We can state on what muscle, or inside what bone
our centres of attention are co-ordinated
with all the separate parts of the body.
This enables us to co-ordinate all the movements of these parts.
The centres can even co-ordinate all movements with our lung and skin breathing.
The outgoing breath supports all our expression in movement and in sound.

But we often make the mistake of imagining
that the centres of attention are extremely busy,
awakening the feeling of the supports,
ordering and directing movements
and co-ordinating and controlling them.
This is not so.
The centres of attention stay in their place
inside the cerebellum,
enfolded around the spinal chord.

75

The centres never move.
The function of the organ of attention
is wholly receptive.
The centres of this organ do not go in search
of the parts of our body which need support.
The part which needs support must seek it,
and make the centres of attention feel
where they are situated and how they function.
Also in what direction they sustain movements.
The centres of attention are always open
receiving demands for support,
absorbing, assimilating and creating
a consciousness of support in our whole body.
Therefore we should never follow with our attention
a movement in its expressive direction.
Everything that is expressed by our movements
mirrors the directions of the movements
in all the brain-cells.
That we, carried by the breath of space from the centre of gravity,
may feel how the basic creative expression, expresses itself
by the directions of our movements in space.

Part III

Life

Life does reveal itself in lives
so varied in form, so infinite in number,
and none alike, which come and change and go
upon the endless flow of time.

Expression of time-less infinity
threading the moments of eternity
through finite form.

What is Life?

Life is a function in the human body.
It is the *basic* function in our body.
The organ of this function is the centre of balance of our form:
the centre of gravity.

From this centre works the process of growth in the body.
The infant becomes adult.
And then the function goes on,
and works to extend and intensify our emanation
towards all sides into outside space.
Extending, intensifying thereby
the workings of our creative possibilities in space around.
That we may establish communion
with all the human beings we meet,
and with objects we touch.

This will enable us to further evolution on this planet,
and create harmonious communities of human beings,
and perfect balance in the body of the human race.

Only in the perfectly balanced community of the whole human race,
can be born a consciousness of the totally receptive state of human bodies,
able to receive all the gifts and accept them,
and to create balance and order
in our human relationship with the earth.

Consciousness of Life

To live, is to have a consciousness of life in every moment.
Life is a gift.
We do not create life ourselves.
Life reveals itself in us
by a constant simultaneous movement
of gathering and radiating of life's Essence.

Read again the first poems in this book.
"Remember that all form is but movement",
and try to undergo this creative movement of life.
This will call you to the Centre of your living body
from where creative Essence,
from the source of life
flows like the water of a well.
It flows towards all sides
through every particle of your body,
cleansing, renewing all substances,
carrying the constant flow of life-force
through your whole form,
carrying all your movements,
and all your expressions in sound and words.
So you will be able to manifest
how Essence creates and re-creates substances.

There are only Three Fundamental States of Being

These three basic states
are intimately united.
One of them is ever present,
underlying the two other states.
It is —
the *Fundamental, Natural, Interrogative state.*

The Three Fundamental States of Being   I

There are only three states of being.
They form a trinity, born out of One.
One fundamental state is always present.
Whilst the two others manifest
in endless variety of expression.

The fundamental state
varies also in infinite shades
of expression.
We call this fundamental state
the interrogative state.
Because we, as human beings,
alive in this relative world,
can never know
what will happen
in the next moment.

The Three Fundamental States of Being   II

The structure and the functioning of our body
is founded on a basis of total receptivity.
Because the whole of our form,
for its psychic and physical existence,
is from its centre, open and receptive
for psychic nourishment and physical food.

The whole body is,
and always should be
in the interrogative state,
open towards outside space
surrounding it.

Only in this receptive attitude
of the whole body,
can we become aware of
what to do, or not to do in the moment.

Being in this interrogative state,
does not mean putting questions
to persons outside,
nor even to oneself.
For if you put a question,
you are already busy
with a certain problem,
expecting certain possibilities
for its solution.

This means that you are not really prepared
to listen towards within.
Inner listening creates
an inner silence
and natural breathing.
The thorax then is open.
The front part of the phrenos is free.
You feel the stomach pit.
The outer borders of the phrenos stay apart
to left and right.
The floating ribs descend, seeking support
on the back of the hipbones.
We can feel tension in the central muscle,
in those parts of the muscle
which are attached
to both sides of the lower side-ribs.

The interrogative state
has endless shades of expression.
We may be anticipating, or wondering,
attentive, or not understanding,
indignant, or amazed,
uncertain, wavering,
or joyfully accepting
an unexpected gift.
Thus we discover that the expression of the interrogative state
varies from moment to moment.

The Three Fundamental States of Being   III

The interrogative state is the basic state of being;
all the time open to inner revelation, and interrogation.
Soul, mind and body at-one,
stay wide open,
even while the two other fundamental states of being
come into expression.

The interrogative state should be
our natural state of being
in every moment.
Our bodily attitude will then reveal this,
by our side-ribs staying open.

We have learned already
to keep the side-ribs open
by practising natural breathing.
Prana-breathing passes through all the articulations,
especially in the cavities of the thigh-bones,
and in the sockets of the upper-bones.

Your bodily attitude will by and by,
quite naturally
express the interrogative state.

When you become active –
making a decision,
deciding to accept
or to do something –
you enter into
the affirmative state.

Then the tension in the central muscle –
while the side-ribs stay open
in the interrogative state –
extends in forward direction,
along the outer borders
of the phrenos,
to where the muscle is attached
to the frontal side-ribs.

So the tension of the interrogative state
is maintained
during the affirmative state.
Because,
when you have acted,
spoken or accepted something,
and *even while* acting,
speaking or accepting,
you will still
in your inner self,
be wondering, awaiting, asking,
what will be the result of –
or the reactions to –
what you did or said,
or were willing to accept
or going to do.

We now know and can feel –
and know for sure, by this sensing and feeling –
the extended tension
necessary while we express
all shades of approval.

It is the attitude
of a human being
expressing in gesture and movement:
"yes".

The movement expressing:
"yes",
will start from this backward support,
on the support given our head
on the atlas vertebra;
marking its beginning movement
by a bouncing movement from backward,
into the movement forward-downward
"yes".
The tension of the central muscle
revealing and translating
the third basic condition of being,
when you must express
that you do not wish to act,
nor join in action,
and must say "no",
to something or somebody.
The tension from the interrogative state
will spread
backwards,
towards the roots of the phrenos.

You will lean in your back,
and from the spine your back will spread.
We may call this state:
a negative state.
A state in which
we do not wish
to act.
Expressing: no, not, never, nowhere,
the tension of interrogation
goes on,
because in you remains the question:
how will the other react
if I do not accept,
or do not join
in action.

The tension of negation in the phrenos
will make you lean in your back,
and spread from the spine
to left and right.

And will create the attitude and gesture
of the head on the top of the spine:
saying silently: "no".
Moving from left to right,
and vice versa.
On your outgoing breath,
you may speak and say:
"no".

84

The Interrogative State   I

The interrogative state is the most natural state of being.
We cannot know the future, nor even what the next moment will bring.
Therefore, in our inner being we are in constant need
of listening towards within.

We must awaken our attention,
which resides receptive in the lower border
of our skull-base,
and stays, even if not active, always interrogative.
When listening towards within
our attention from this base,
will open and direct itself towards below.
It will create in the whole body
the fundamental state of being:
the interrogative state.

The interrogative state works in us
by opening the lower ribs,
to which the outer borders of the diaphragm
are attached,
finding psychic and physical support
against the lower backribs.

It is true — but we may have forgotten —
that the diaphragm, besides massaging the organs in the pelvis,
which sucks the air into the lungs,
is also the muscle
which translates all psychic tensions
into actions and expressions,
by three basic physical tensions
of the diaphragm.

It is thus we can express
all inner movements of emotion,
all inspiration and ideas and intentions,
in three basic expressions for all our moods,
infinitely varied.

The Interrogative State   II

The interrogative state creates
a very special attitude in our body.
The foremost part
of the central muscle
which covers our stomach,
can, when we breathe out,

freely move our stomach backwards
towards the spine.
And we will feel,
just underneath the breastbone,
how this movement
creates the stomach-pit.

The lower sideribs stay open, wide apart
to left and right while breathing out,
leaving the stomach free
to descend and approach the spine.
Then the breath flows freely out,
and will carry our sonorous expressions
through the vocal chords,
in sounds and words.

The muscle covering the lower back and side-ribs,
should seek support towards below on the hip-bones.
We have the tendency to lift these muscles.
Alas, we lift nearly all our inner organs
away from their supports.

Bhagavad Gita: Chapter 5, Verse 27.
"Having left external contact outside;
with the vision within the eyebrows;
having balanced the ingoing and outgoing
breaths that flow through the nostrils."

The Interrogative State   III

When we continue creating in the two sensitive regions
in our skull-base, the feeling of space,
keeping these centres wide apart;
not only will this simple movement
open our lower side-ribs,
and so give us the possibility
of breathing naturally,
but it will in the lower pelvis, stretch
the abdominal, transversal muscles,
descending from the breast-bone
towards the pubis
relaxed, free from shortening by contraction,
keeping all the organs in the pelvis
supported.

Thus the region between the thorax and the pelvis
will be freed from strain,
there will be no pressure underneath the wind-pipe.

And the throat stays open,
and lets the air go out freely.

The air changes its direction
against the throat-wall,
at the back of the mouth.
The air mounts into the throat
and then is directed forward,
entering the mouth,
supported, as we said,
against the throat-wall
behind the mouth.

The tongue stays free from all contraction,
and rests in the lower jaw-bone,
spreading and forming a large cup.

We now will give our attention
to the three basic states of being
in relation to expression.

The Interrogative State   IV

Let us direct our attention again
to the state we have created
within:
the interrogative state.
This restores natural breathing,
and awakes the feeling of all the supports
in our back, in our pelvis,
and against the throat-wall.

The interrogative state creates
an inner silence.
Our attention will open inwardly.
In this attentive silence
inspiration, ideas, intentions
will mount and will tell us
what to express in the moment.

There is the natural state of interrogation,
which is, and ever stays alive during all our changing moods.
The outer borders of our diaphragm
attached to the lower side-ribs move apart.
This opening movement spreads through the whole body.

87

Do not Put Questions!

Do not *put* questions!
Be the question in the moment.
Why do you wish to see yourself 'doing'?
Preconceived actions
mentally controlled,
interfere
with passing thoughts and images.

We should fulfil our own destiny.
We can only know how
when we stay within ourselves
at-one with the creative force of Infinite Space.
It is quite natural for our whole form
to be open and listen
to what is given to us in every moment.
Inspiration, and creative intelligence directing
our soul, spirit and body, at-one
in what we do or say,
in all that we express.
We should be totally present.

To put questions is fixing thoughts and words
either in our prayers or to persons around us,
or to ourselves within, or to God.
This will make it impossible for us to enter
into the interrogative state.
Born into this world, we can still stay
in our human form intimately related
with the Presence of the Creator.
This Presence is creating in every moment
what must be done or said,
in order to fulfil in that very moment
our own unique destiny in the Universe.

Part IV

Space is the Only Creative, Expressive Essence

I ask you to feel again, and understand
that Space is the only Creative, Expressive Essence.
Space is Infinite, Omnipresent, Eternal.
It is the eternal aspect of Space
which reveals our first dimension –
the dimension of Time.
Revelation manifests in duration.
Time thereby becomes the carrier of all
manifested form in the Universe.
The carrier of all movement.
Remember that all form is but movement.

Space Movements are not Movements

Space movements are *not* movements.
They are the Presence of Infinite Essence in form.

Man can become aware of this Presence
in the very first dimension of our form –
the flow of Time.
This is the birth of rhythm,
on which Infinity
is threading eternal moments
in finite form.

This is simple and logical.
The manifestation of the Essence of Life
in physical form.
There could never be the manifestation
of three dimensional forms
without duration of Time.

Space-Essence

In a centre inside our body –
the centre of gravity,
deep in the pelvis
just in front of the bottom-vertebra
in the sacrum –
creative force
is gathering
all the time,
from all sides.
It is gathering Life's Essence.

91

This Essence is Space.
Space is Creative Essence.
It wishes to reveal
its true being.
It therefore manifests itself
in substance.

All substance
revealing essence
is expressive.

The gathering of Space-Essence
brings to the form all it needs for its being,
for its staying alive.
It distributes all psychic and physical food,
air, drink and impressions,
to sustain body and mind,
and to renew in every moment all substances.
Space-Essence also sustains our creative activities.

On Space-Functions in General

Few people know
that there are space-functions
in the human body.

Science has brought to our attention,
that space is inherent in all movement.
So space moves through our whole form.

Most people do not give enough attention
to these basic facts
underlying our inner being,
and influencing our daily life.

Try to feel
while reading this,
that your whole body is constantly
pervaded by the breath of space.
Thereby kept alive,
and able to move,
carried on the flow
of that Creative Essence.

92

Therefore we should always keep our body open
towards outside space.
From the centre of the body
like a hand opening to receive;
spreading towards left and right,
towards downwards and upwards,
towards back and front.

Then creative breath
passes through the whole form,
through all the cells,
through every fibre,
through all substances,
purifying, strengthening
and renovating them.

The revelation of the infinite Essence of space,
from this centre of balance in our form,
manifests itself by spreading its Essence to all sides
through the whole body.
This may enable us in every moment
and in every situation,
to feel and remember
how this essence supports us,
and helps us to deal
with whatever befalls us —
good or bad.

We need the support of this breath of space
for all our expressions in action and in speech.

One of the Most Important Space-Functions
in the Human Body

From the centre of gravity —
centre of balance in the form —
the breath of space passes
through all the articulations.

First from the centre it goes out
to left and right,
along the lower border of the pelvis,
and breathes through both the sockets of the thighbones.
In the dimension,
which from the centre
spreads to left and right,
the axis of life's breadth in the human body is created,

93

representing the dimension of liberation.
From the spine, the whole body spreads –
as you can feel –
when you stretch.

Do not neglect to undergo and practise,
over and over again,
the movement of stretching.
Feel that your body has two sides,
which from the spine,
must always be felt
in opposite directions.

Everywhere on this earth,
through all ages,
all nations and races
have been trained on the same basis.
All soldiers have been taught
"to put their little fingers
on the scams of their trousers."

You must teach yourself
to do the same in the right way:
from the spine
let your body create
two halves in opposite directions.
You will become free from fear,
from anxiety, and apprehension,
as it was meant to set the warriors free
that they may fearlessly enter into battle.

When you have practised this,
it will be quite easy to realise,
how space-breathing is working
in the two cavities of the thighbones,
low in the pelvis.

From these two cavities breathing starts
through all the other articulations,
because from there the breath of space
starts downwards and upwards,
to all the other articulations in the body.
First downwards through the knee-holes,
and further downwards through the ankles,
and then on through the feet,
and on and on through all the articulations
of the toes.

At the same time,
space-breathing goes upwards
through the trunk.
The breath of space
plays through the sockets
underneath the shoulders.
And from there continues
downwards in the arms.

Downwards-upwards in the body represents
the dimension of its height.
The dimension of the height of a body
is its dimension of balance.
So now we have experienced
the presence of two dimensions in our body —
breadth and height.

Executing these exercises we can work
our liberation and our balance.

We must still awake in you
the consciousness of space-breathing
through the articulation
of the head resting on the spine;
and the feeling of its working
in the joint articulations
of the vertebrae.

For this important space-working
through the spine,
we have created special exercises.
You will learn to practise them later,
when we have awakened
the feeling of your relationship
to your back, and to backward-space.

Concentration, Radiation, Meditation

Let us open our minds
in order to understand this movement,
which is ever keeping us alive.

Let us discover how
the concentration of life-force
takes place inside of us.
We must give this movement room in our inner space
so that it may spread through us.

If we *do* this movement ourselves,
it would cause a contraction in our mind and body.
The movement of concentration enters our form
from infinite space around us.
Its pure activity does not demand from us inactivity.
We should become *passive*, wholly receptive.
The creation of this passive state
asks for a very deep and full activity,
to meet and receive the creative movement
of the concentration of life-force inside of us,
which then *simultaneously* radiates freely from the centre
through our whole form,
back into infinite space.

Be Wholly Receptive in Order to be Wholly Expressive

Bones, though alive by the constant movement
of renovation of their cells and substances,
do not move.
They are moved by our muscles.
Muscles, although made to move the bones,
only do so when directed by the nervous system.

The nervous system *directs* our movements
created by psychic tensions,
caused by the necessity of emotional and spiritual
expression.
Spiritual necessity of expression creates ideas.
Emotional necessity of expression creates acts.

Sometimes the spirit moves us,
sometimes the soul.
Or both together function in our form at the same time, and play
on the chords of our expressive instrument:
the body.
We call our "soul",
that which within us causes the necessity
of emotional expression.
We call our "spirit",
the same deep necessity to express
the awareness of ideas.

Emotional expression translates itself mostly in acts,
in attitudes, gestures and movements.
Spiritual expression creates in us ideas,
which by creative intelligence and thought,

96

lead us to communicate with others in words,
spoken or written down.

If we understand and realize
what this prose-poem tells us in the first verse,
it is evident that we should learn
to play on the chords of our nervous system.

In schools and institutes,
what are we taught to do?
They teach us the *outer* effects
of movements and speech.
The *results* of the creative process
of expression in movements
are shown to us and impressed upon us.
Watching results,
we form mental pictures of the movements.
Then we are asked to imitate
these outer effects,
and to repeat mechanically these movements
in order to train the body.
Thereby we necessitate
a constant directive control by the brain
of the movements we execute.

We then lose all creative possibility
of expression.
Our movements are robbed
of life's Essence.

It is the same with speech
when we talk to others or write to them.
We learn to train the voice.
People hear all that we say.
But cannot and do not listen,
as our intonation misses
life's direct vibration and inner rhythm.
We then *act* feeling and passion.
We force the voice, its pitch,
and strain its accentuation.

How then can we receive and safeguard
the gift of life's Creative Essence?

Space-breathing in the Vertebrae

Sit down in a comfortable chair.
Relax.
And do not try to stretch your back.
Let yourself go.
Your spine is bent.
Let your elbows be supported by your knees,
and with your hands support your head.

You know that in the base of the skull,
just in the middle of its lower border,
where the top of the spinal column
enters the skull-base, there is a small opening.
This opening is situated
between the centres of your attention.
These centres are to left and right,
situated very low in the skull-base,
behind the cavities of the ears.

The small hole in the middle of the skull-base
descends around the atlas,
the topmost vertebra of the spine.
Thus the whole weight of the head
finds its support upon the spine.

We hope that you still sit
supporting your head with your hands,
your elbows on your knees,
eyes closed.
We hope you have been able
to follow all we told you
about the articulation
of your head on the atlas vertebra.

Feel your head rests
upon the topmost vertebra of your spine.
We think you now know exactly
where in space your skull-base is,
also the back of your head,
and feel the articulation of the head on the spine.

Do not try to focus and fix
what you are seeing.
Just sense
where the parts we mentioned
are present in space.

Then descend in your relaxed back,
through your neck and vertebrae
towards the bottom of your pelvis,

until you have established
the linking of your attention
with the bottom-vertebra,
from where the coccyx starts.
And try to sense and feel
the seat of the chair you sit on,
underneath that vertebra
in the middle of the sacrum.

Feel at each side of that vertebra
the cushions of the buttock-muscles.
Keep these muscles apart,
so that the sacrum-vertebra may touch the seat.
And accept the support the seat offers
to your sitting body.

Intensify the sensing and the feeling
all your attention has absorbed.
Do this as if you were on the point of falling asleep.
Keep the feeling alive
of the support the chair gives you.
And accept the support.

Then plant the vertebra in the border of the sacrum
firmly on the seat.
The seat becomes the foundation
on which we now shall build up the spine.
Plant all the vertebrae
one by one, soldered and united in the sacrum,
forming the strong backbone in your pelvis,
firmly on the foundation of the seat,
with a strong tendency towards below,
in the direction of the support of the seat.

The wall of the backbone is now
upright on the seat,
seeking the support of the back of the chair.
Give attention and feel how this wall of your backbone
reaches your waist,
and lean against the back of the chair.

From the waist on,
put one vertebra after another on top of this wall.
The weight of each vertebra goes towards below
and to each vertebra underneath.
So you build a pillar:
first till the waist,
then behind the stomach,

and between the shoulder blades,
adding all the time
one vertebra on top of the lower one.

The pillar is supported by the seat
which you keep feeling underneath.
Then you go on
putting the neck-vertebrae
one on top of another,
till at last you reach the atlas vertebra.
Then the pillar carries the head.

If thus you build your spine
on the firm support of the seat,
you will without effort
sit upright in the chair.
Perhaps leaning against its back,
finding an extra support in the back
besides the support on the seat of the chair.

The breath of space is passing
through all the vertebrae
and through the articulation of the head
on top of the atlas,
joining the space-breathing
through all the other articulations in the body.

You may remember how the breath of Prana
from the articulations of the thighbones,
went downwards towards knees and ankles.
And upwards towards the heads
of both the upper armbones,
and then in the opposite direction downwards
through elbows, wrists and fingers.

Add the feeling and the sensation
of the Prana-breathing through these articulations,
to the breath of Prana passing through the spine,
and through all the articulations of the head on the spine.

And then let your attention detach itself
from creating and leading the exercise.
Let it rest in its own centres.
There it will stay, attentive as its nature is,
but totally relaxed and thereby receive
the after-effects of the exercise which will keep alive
for still awhile,
the feeling of the Prana-breathing
through all the articulations.
And you will be sitting upright in your chair.

Backward-Downward   I

There is only one way to go
for our attention.
And its direction we should know.
It is backward-downward.

Weight of the body, and the weight of worries
into the back and skull-base they must go.
And then descend towards the earth, so
backward-downward.

To lie down, to sit, to squat,
we, to perform these movements, go
backward-downward.

Our food and drink to taste,
our breath and fragrance to smell,
it all comes and enters our mouth,
and underneath the nostrils
on the flow of time,
it all will go
backward-downward.

And if we wish or need to rest, and so
will fall asleep, the movement
of sleep will take us, and wipe out
the consciousness of self, and take us
to the source of life
backward, then downward.

In meditation, seeking to dive
deep downward towards the source of life,
entering into a state of being,
we must direct ourselves and go
backward-downward.

Life fully lived, accomplishing
its destiny, will bring us back
to rest upon the earth, and carry us
backward-downward.

So –
there is only one way to go
for our attention,
and its direction we should know.

Backward-downward.

Backward-Downward   II

There is also only one movement,
which by itself
should go on and on
in these directions
all the time —
backward-downward.

It is an opening movement
of the doors of our senses,
exposing the sensitive skins
inside our ears, our nose, our mouth,
and the skins of the eyes, the retinas,
to the incoming tide of impressions,
reaching along the strings of the nerves
to the centres of our attention,
low down in the skull-base
behind the ears.

Our eyes will close, and we enter
into another world
where we no longer see
the incoming images.
In our brain starts a hazy feeling.
And we feel only the atmosphere
of our inner life.

So we learn in our physical body
to refine physical sensations.
And when these physical sensations
lead us into the world of our feeling,
into a deeper and more ethereal region,
we then descend and go downward
inside our back,
to the lower border
of the sacrum.

Thus we are carried
in front of this sacral bone,
to the centre of our being,
to the fountain of life.

It is the flow of life-force,
the breath of space.
We move on this flow of time.
Dive deep.

Backward-Downward III

Try to perfect this movement of backward-downward of your attention.
Learn to direct it, and thereby to master it.
Dive first into outside space in front of your eyes,
into the stream of space carrying you
through the doors of your senses,
into your inside space.

Sense and feel the directions of this movement intensely.
Merge into the expressive essence of space within,
which pervades all bodily substances of your form,
in order that you may become creative.

Try to attain this creative state of being
at the centre of your body.
Try from there to live and learn,
to imagine and to think,
to do, to act, to speak,
to express all
that from the fountain of life
starts to spread in your physical form,
and wishes to become visible, and to vibrate
in the sonorous gestures of what you say or sing,
in your laugh, in your cry, and in your call.

Because you need to be creative
on all occasions that present themselves in life,
when you must show
that man can live creatively,
even when he is old,
or weakened by the many attacks on him
in this our relative world.
These attacks cause us to be in need
of that creative force,
which in our form keeps us alive,
as it keeps alive in the whole Universe
every form, however small or frail.

Dimension

By now you are able
to gather from within, knowledge through the sensation
of where lie situated, in your inner space,
the different organs and parts of your body.

You may even feel the movements of the functions,
in and through these organs,
and the *directions* of these functional movements
according to the structure of the organs.
Then you can begin to establish, with absolute exactness,
the natural order in your bodily domain.

The natural order in a form can only be maintained,
when the central organ by its function,
co-ordinates all other functions in that form.

You know many exercises
which start from that centre of balance of the whole form,
the centre of gravity.
It maintains not only the balance of the bodily weight,
it is the centre, which maintains the union
of physical and psychic balance.

We should feel and know this by bodily sensation,
and from there sense each organ and each part of our form.
Also in what direction all the substances
of the parts and organs are renewed,
and their functions sustained.
All these natural processes can be felt,
by our centres of attention absorbing
the inner impressions of their movements in inside space.
On this basis you can practise every time
a new sensation and deeper awareness of true being.

You can practise the different exercises,
and develop this consciousness,
and restore the true relationship
between the three dimensions of your form.

Many texts in the Holy Scriptures of the world
will help you to understand,
and they will work, and create in your understanding
the realization of the presence
of four dimensions in your three dimensional body.

Your three dimensional body could not manifest
without the first dimension of space,
its living breath creating the dimension of time
of duration.
Without this breath, and this dimension
not a single form in the universe
could reveal its divine origin, and presence
in form.

St. Paul writes in Ephesians, chapter 3, verses 17 to 19.
"That Christ may dwell in your hearts by faith;
that ye being rooted and grounded in love,
may be able to comprehend with all saints
what is the *breadth*, and *length* and *depth* and *height*.
And to know the love of Christ,
which passeth knowledge,
that ye might be filled with all the fulness of God."

The Vedas: "Be not One-Sided, Be to All Sides"

"Be not one-sided, be to all sides."
In order that we may live according to the teaching of the Vedas,
let us try to understand the meaning of this teaching.

Let us first state that in everyday life
we are in contact with other beings and things
in one direction only –
namely in the direction where these beings or things
find themselves in space around us.
Thus we may consider that all contact in space is,
and ever will be – "one-sided."
Then how can we ever be "to all sides"?

We are always very much aware of outside space.
Now let us imagine
that somebody or something approaches us
from one side in space.
Its image enters into our inner space
by the doors of our senses
and is absorbed by the centres of our attention.
Then it descends to our centre of gravity,
causing impressions and an inner experience.

If we let this happen
our response will start from the centre of gravity.
From there, this response will be carried
in movements and words
on the breath of space throughout our whole form,
and will emanate to all sides.
Thus our actions will in this way "be to all sides".

Mastering Emotional Expression

You have learned to spread
and to lean backwards.
Spreading outwards from the spine,
and then dropping the weight of the trunk, and of the arms and the head,

105

in the back in which you lean.
The weight drops downwards to the lower border of the sacral bone,
just behind the articulations of the thigh-bones.
It descends along these thigh-bones to the outside of the heels.
The outer borders of both the feet
are ever there, when moving,
to carry the weight of the whole body
on this firm support.

Then all the organs in the body can drop their weight.
The bowels, spleen and liver,
the stomach and the heart,
the lungs and all the organs in the throat,
the centres of attention in the skull-base.
The cortex and the brain-cells will then relax.

Only when we keep the organs downwards,
will the brain stop dominating,
commanding and controlling,
our psychic and physical behaviour;
thereby mechanising our movements
and disturbing our functions.

Emotions cause a sudden lifting of the organs,
of the stomach and the heart.
They block the throat,
create havoc in the brain,
and break the link with the source of life.

To master these disastrous effects of our emotions,
we must let the weight of all the organs drop
in trunk and head, and in the arms and legs.

If we ever wish to arrive at letting emotion –
that is the necessity of expression –
spread creatively throughout our body;
we must not forget that expression is a movement
which mounts in our back,
and liberates in us the function of memory,
opening the storehouse of past experience.
This movement mounts towards the centres of attention.
And from there, it lets our intellectual capacities
partake in the creative movements
of our expression.
All our intellectual centres in the brain
will then be at the service
of our creative expression.

Our Relationship to Backward Space, Inside and Outside the Body

Our back, our pelvis, and our shoulder-blades,
and all along the spine, and in the head
behind the ear-lobes in the skull-base –
all this belongs to the back part of our body.
All these parts are directed into backward space,
into space behind us.

In the nerves, in the fibres of the muscles,
in the bones of spine and back-ribs,
in the back of the head, and of the sacrum,
and in the heels,
there is no forward movement.
When moving forward, all these back parts
are the supports upon which the forward movements bounce.
We must establish the backward feeling in those parts,
and create a relationship with space behind us.

In the back parts of our body,
all our experience gathered in the past
lies dormant in the depths of our pelvis,
at the bottom of our spine.
From there we should learn to master creative expression
as from the centre all we will need to express,
will mount in that back part of our body
in spine and nerves.
In this centre our past is linked with the future
without a break.

Balance – The Relationship between Weight and Support

To move, is to play with the weight of the body.
In order to keep the body in balance
you need supports.

Thus balance asks you to know, and to feel
the intimate relationship between the weight of a body
and its supports.

In this relationship the amount of the weight of the volume
plays no role.
It will be easier to balance a beam,
which can only be lifted with the help of a crane,
than to balance a small light feather,
which has hardly any weight.

The weight must spread on the support
however small.
The weight must not be contracted, and one who seeks balance,
must learn to spread the weight of the body
first in the back.
Spread the weight away from the spine.
In the brain, in the base of the skull,
in the nose, in the chin, in the mask,
in the whole head.
Balance the head on the small support of the atlas,
the top-most vertebra.

From the top of the spine,
the body spreads to right and to left
into two halves equal in form.

Try to feel right and left inside the body,
feel their pure spatial expression
expanding from the spine in opposite directions
According to the natural structure of the body,
the whole body is a spatial expression in six directions.

Direction is pure spatial expression.

Deep down in the pelvis, the weight of the trunk
descends in the back, and spreads to right and to left
behind the thighbones.

Let your legs support
the back of your trunk in which you lean,
and spread all the muscles,
like wings
that carry you
in balance.
Even when, in the wonderful art of the classical ballet
you move like a gentle bird spreading its pinions;
or stand in balanced vibration of beauty,
on the smallest support
of one single toe.

All Expression is Movement

All expression is movement.
The movements begin with space inside our body
passing through the different parts of the body.
They become visible in our attitudes, in our facial expression,
in our gestures, and in our movements in outside space.

All these movements we might call
our language of movement.
We can also express ourselves in song and speech,
in the language of sounds and words.
The basic expression of all movements is direction.
Without movement, no visible or audible expression is possible.
Even if the body is seriously injured,
the attitudes and facial expression
however hampered will be expressive.
Because as long as we are alive,
there will be in us the emanation of life's force,
which means that the movement of life,
by its concentration-radiation of life's force
will sustain this emanation until we die.
It is this concentration-radiation, the breath of life
which carries all movements of the human body.
All visible and audible expressions
depend on this basic movement of the breath of life.
The essence of this breath is space.
The basic functions in the human body are space functions.
The purely creative expressive essence in form is direction.
The basic meaning of all we express
in the languages of movement and sound,
is expressed in the inner direction of these movements.
Most of this is taught
in the Natya Shastra, in the Bhagavad Gita,
in the Tao Te Ching, and in many of Chuang T'se's poems.
In the Oriental civilisations, there was
an anthropological consciousness of human evolution.
The ordinary people, in many ways
were still near to the primates;
were toiling to defend their territory and housing,
were tilling the land in order to have food and drink
for themselves and their offspring.
They lived, concentrating on having and holding things,
on capturing and exploiting.
But there were those conscious of evolution,
following and practising the teachings of great Masters,
like Buddha and the Rishis,
who wrote the Vedas and the Shastras.
There were the poets of the epic poems,
the Mahabarata, and the Ramayana.
There were social institutions, rites, ceremonies
and artists performing on the stage.
The responsibility of these artists was to open
the bodies and minds of the audience,
creating in the people the interrogative state.
Therefore the artists themselves, had to enter
into that basic interrogative state;

and by their acting, and the texts of their plays
they had to answer the questions which were
working in the minds of the people,
while the play went on.
In these civilised communities there still was in those who governed,
a clear consciousness and knowledge
of the problems, and their solutions.
The artists were naturally gifted in the techniques of their professions.
That is the reason that the Natya Shastra
does not explain these techniques.
You can find them in this book of self re-education,
as we, like these artists who lived so long ago
mastered these techniques.
In my husband these techniques were so deeply inborn
that he did not want to discuss them.
Within myself, I had a deep consciousness of these techniques,
but they were silenced by Western influences.
My gifts were greatly developed
by the teaching of Inayat Khan,
and by the constant and intimate collaboration
with my husband.
It became a conscious process within,
therefore I try to teach these techniques as best I can.
I know that in the depth of being
and in the body of every human creature,
there is the Presence,
and always a vague awareness of the "State of Being".
To be able to teach,
I must let the state of each pupil
enter into my deepest consciousness.
Listening to the Presence within myself,
I will then know
by life's breath, and its space working in my body and mind,
how to awake in a pupil his "State of Being".
Then the pupil begins to feel
that he can become linked within himself
to his own Master.
The Presence within him will teach him by inspiration,
by creative breath,
the support of all creative expression in movement and in speech.

Let the Presence of the Creator

Let the Presence of the Creator,
whom we will not imprison in our human concepts,
who is Omnipresent in his Creation
not moving, but Being,

inspire us to express what He reveals
in and through the substances
of the nervous system in our body.

I can state that the nervous threads in our brain
as well as in our bodies,
in the perfect balance of the nervous system
cross in different places.
The first crossing takes place
in the most backward part of the skull
where the optic nerves
reach the skull-bone in a backward direction,
and then change direction in a downward movement
at the thalamus,
and in that organ cross.

The nervous threads divide their fibres as they cross.
Some move downwards to the motor centres,
and some to the centres of attention.
These threads form a very narrow triangle
a short distance from the top of the atlas vertebra
to the bottom of the skull-base, low in the neck,
they move right and left to both ear-shells,
where soon they reach the inner skins of the tympanums.
There we have already learnt to listen towards within.

At the bottom of the neck a second crossing takes place.
Most of us know this fact,
as we are taught that the left side of the brain
frees the movements of the right side of our body,
and vice versa –
the right side frees the movements of the left side.
This creates the alternation of walking,
one of the very first movements of a human being.
This is the function of the fibres of the nervous threads
which have descended in our brain to these motor centres,
and to the centres of attention.

From these centres, five straight lines descend
in the back part of our neck, in our trunk
to the bottom of our pelvis.
At the very end of the spine,
at the infinite organ of balance –
our centre of gravity –
a last crossing takes place
and descends to both sides of our legs
through our buttock muscles and fascialata,
towards the outer tendons in our knee-holes.
From there the movement descends to our ankle-joints
and the outer heels,

111

finding underneath the soles of our feet
the only outer support –
the earth,
the gift of the Creator to all living creatures,
providing our food, drink, air and support.

As *we* do not perform this crossing of the space movements
we do not need to fix them, supervise them,
apply or control them.
The revelation of the space movements
of the infinite Essence of space,
effortlessly manifests in the perfect union of the two parts
of our nervous system.
These movements escape most of us,
as our awareness has so degenerated.
But the true state of balance can be restored in us.
That is why I have tried to describe the exact happening
to help to recreate this conscious awareness.

In Jodjana's art,
the law of balance was expressed and so apparent.
The perfect unity of opposite directions
in his attitudes and movements.
He called this "symmetry".

The Creator IS in His Creation

The Creator IS in His Creation.
In simple language we can say
that He is OMNIPRESENT.

Man mostly names Him with an adjective,
with numberless adjectives denoting something
which man wants Him to be
in order to fulfil a personal wish,
or to obtain some petty human favour.

As the Creator is everywhere in His Creation.
He does not move.
He is the only Presence which never moves,
and thereby is the only ever present support
in every fibre of all form.

Introduction to the "Supports"

As we express ourselves by movements of the body,
and by the movement of breath in sound exclamations,
in speech and song,
we have very simply to realize that every movement needs support.
We have lost the feeling and consciousness of the supports.
Supports rely on our attention.
It is attention that awakes in the supports
the feeling and consciousness of being present,
and tell us from where a movement starts.

Thus the pure expression
of the directions of these movements is realized.
We must restore the feeling and consciousness of the ever-present link
of our supports and movements, with the centres of attention.

The centres of attention are there, mirroring this link.

The Rotation Axis

On each rotation axis of the four limbs
we can find a series of three supports.
All movements of the hands, of the fingers,
have their support underneath the outer wrist-bone.
This being so, all particles of the physical substances of the hand
seek for support, and receive it underneath the wrist-bone.

The middle finger, the ring-finger and the little finger,
stretch in the left hand outwards to the left,
in the right hand to the right.
From the inside of the middle finger, we can feel
how the index stretches in forward direction.
The thumb has an intimate relationship
with the index –
but the thumb can touch all the other fingers as well.

The fingers start from the wrist-bone
(there are seven small bones that make up the wrist)
and form the hand-cup.
The whole hand can relax
when we stay conscious of the support
underneath the wrist-bone.

Mounting upwards along the rotation axis towards the elbow,
we reach the second support in the arm.

113

It is the elbow-joint between three small bone-heads.
This joint gives support to all substances and all movements
of the forearm.
The forearm can totally relax
when we stay conscious of this support.

All movements of the forearm start from this support.
Moving further upwards, we have to open our attention
towards the insides of the shoulder blades,
to find the support of all the substances and all the movements
of the whole arm.

The three supports as we said,
are linked by the rotation axis,
through which the breath of life sustains the arm movements.
The series of the three supports being the support
of every particle of the arm's substances,
the arm movements become very light,
so that they can express every movement
on any rhythm, quick or slow.

For the legs we will find the same principles apply.
The two series of three supports in the legs
are all in their rotation axes.

The toes start in the foot from the heel,
and find the support for all their movements and all their substances,
underneath the outer heel,
and behind the outer anklebone.

The art of dance in the Orient
is as rich and varied in expression,
in the movements with the feet,
as in the movements of the hands and fingers.

The weight of the legs, and the whole body
is sustained by the same support,
the outside support of the ground underneath the feet.
But the movements and the substances of the lower legs
are supported by the outer tendons
forming the border of the cup
underneath the articulation of the knee.

We can find the third support
for all the movements and substances of the thighs,
in the rotation axis which mounts along the outer backside
underneath the thighbones.
These supports are behind the heads and necks of the thighbones,
and inside the sockets of these bones in the pelvis.

The Three Axes of the Spatial Skeleton
Six Directions; The Supports

The human body has three dimensions.
From its centre of gravity
there is full concentration-radiation of Creative Essence,
which in a three-dimensional form
becomes visible in our individual emanation.
And in the living body manifests itself by balance.
Our three-dimensional form
has three axes, each axis being
a spreading movement from the centre
in opposite directions.
A vertical axis: downward-upward;
a horizontal axis spreading: backward-forward;
another horizontal axis spreading: left and right.

The three together form our *spatial skeleton*.

So, for our communion with other forms in space,
we become expressive in infinite variety,
and infinite co-ordination,
in six directions.

Each axis offers for expression, movements
from the centre in two opposite directions.
Thus each movement starts on its track
and *finds support* in the opposite direction.
All *upward* movement is supported from *below*.
The earth is our fundamental outside support.
All *forward* movement must start
and be supported in *our back*.
Our movements to the *left*, find
their counter-weight and support in the *right side* of our body,
and vice versa.

There are in addition to the outside supports
of the earth underneath,
and the central psychic support of our centre of gravity
in the bottom of the pelvis,
thirty three supports which lie in the back of our body,
all united and co-ordinated in a downward direction.

The central psychic support of the centre of gravity,
in co-ordination with our two centres of attention,
guards the perfect psychic and physical balance in our form.
We can learn to master
the thirty three supports we mentioned,
because the organ of our attention,

and all the motor capacities
are situated in the cerebellum
in the back of the head.

There is a logical relationship
between our capacity to move
and the centres of attention,
co-ordinating in a downward direction
the thirty three *descending supports*
in the back of our trunk and limbs.
We can *feel* these thirty three supports
as thirty three keys of a key-board
on which moving, we can improvise
melodies of movements and chords.

We can play on this keyboard like a pianist
not hindered by the number of the keys.
We can then listen to our movements
which will tell us how we move,
and how this wonderful flow of movement
takes place in our inner space.

Our centres of attention open,
and all the brain cells and brain centres relax and listen.
We have only to ask:
"How does it feel, how does it sound?"
And we will be carried on the flowing rhythm
of the melodies and the chords of movement.

Those who see us move, will see these improvisations
and live with us the manifestation of this creative experience.

DIAGRAM OF THE 33 SUPPORTS
AND ROTATION AXIS
IN THE BACK OF THE BODY

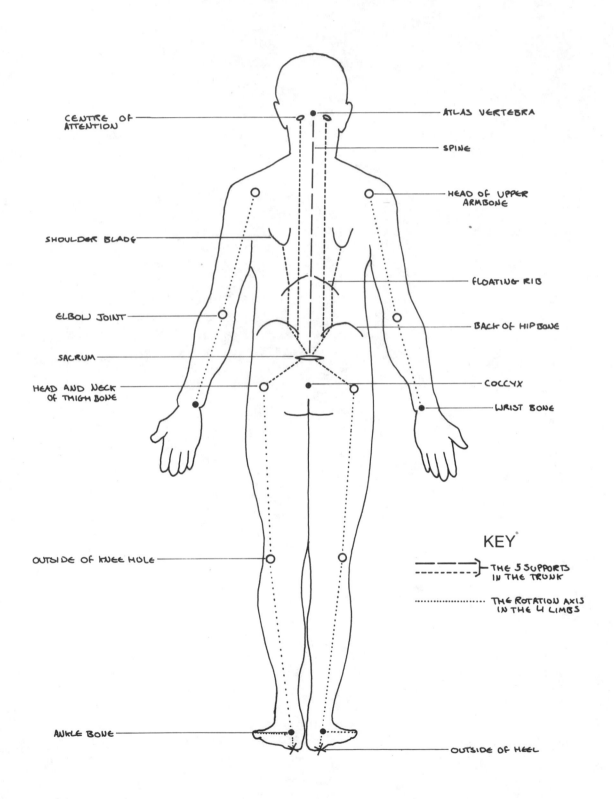

CENTRE OF ATTENTION

ATLAS VERTEBRA

SPINE

HEAD OF UPPER ARMBONE

SHOULDER BLADE

FLOATING RIB

ELBOW JOINT

BACK OF HIP BONE

SACRUM

HEAD AND NECK OF THIGH BONE

COCCYX

WRIST BONE

OUTSIDE OF KNEE HOLE

ANKLE BONE

OUTSIDE OF HEEL

KEY

———— THE 5 SUPPORTS IN THE TRUNK

.... THE ROTATION AXIS IN THE 4 LIMBS

The Eleven Series of Three Supports

Let us now open our attention
to all the central supports
of the eleven series of three supports in the body.

We will begin with the series
of five united supports in the trunk.
The whole length of the spine is a central support,
giving a support on its topmost vertebra
in an upward backward direction
at the centre back of our skull.
And at the bottom of the spine
there is the support above the coccyx
pointing in downward-forward direction.
Feeling backward-upward at the top,
and downward-forward at the bottom,
will create balance when we move in space.

In both the legs,
the central support of the series of three supports
lie at the outside of the knee-holes,
from where there is a relationship
downwards behind the ankles
and underneath the outside of the heels.
In upward direction, the central support of the knee-holes
sustain the heads and necks of the thigh-bones.
These bones are supported
against the backside of the cavities
in which these bones lie.

The central support in the arms
lies in the elbow-joints.
From there downwards
we find the supports underneath the wrist-bones,
from where all movements
of the hands and fingers are sustained.
The elbow-joints also sustain
the movements of the upper armbone,
finding support inside the shoulder-blades.

The movements of the arms and hands
are supported by the legs.
We find at the outside of our back
there are the series of five supports
linking the movements of the arms and legs.

The central support of the series of five supports
lies in the waist,

where the floating ribs tend
to find support in a downward direction
on the back part of the hip-bones.
This movement continues downwards towards the back-bone
where the cavities in which
the heads and necks of the thigh-bones find support.
In an upward direction the central back plane of support
sustains the arm movements
which from the top support inside the shoulder blades
carries all our arm movements.

Create a mental clearness about the axes in the four limbs
which are linked by the series of five supports in the trunk.
The movements uniting the rotation axes in arms and legs
are co-ordinated in a simple and most wonderful way.

From the inside of the shoulder blades,
the series of three supports in the arms
descend through the supports of the elbow-joints
to underneath the wrist bones.

In the trunk we find at the outside of the body
the series of three supports
linking the movements of arms and legs.
The supports from the inside of the shoulder blades
descend through the supports linking the ribs to the hipbones
and then downwards towards the supports
in the cavities of the thighbones.

Space Workings are the Workings of Constant Renovation

Space workings are the workings of constant renovation.
Happenings of which we become aware by impressions.
Space workings are at the same time
workings of constant revelation.
They wish to be revealed
to be expressed.
As happenings they tell themselves to our awareness
by impressions,
as revelation they wish to be told.
They are our State of Being,
of Being alive.
They find space
they find place
in all forms manifested in the Universe.

Further Information about the Centre of Gravity

The centre of gravity supports all psychic tensions
spiritual and emotional.
It creates the physical supports we need
for our movements and speech,
by which we translate
these psychic tensions
in movements and words.

In our body are thirty-three supports:
for the breath, for the head,
and as we saw, for all movements
of our trunk, legs, and arms.

The whole weight of our body
is supported by the earth;
and by other outside supports
like boulders, tree-trunks;
and in the house,
by floors, beds and mattresses,
chairs, cushions and carpets.

Our attention should always search
for supports;
and stay conscious of them
whilst moving.

The supports never seek for things to support.
They are just there.
And we,
we have to search for them.
And accept their service,
as they accept our weight.
Understand and realize this.

Stay with full attention
always directed towards the supports,
in the direction *opposite*
to the direction of the movements.

Part V

Re-education of the Senses

To learn to master our attention,
and let it recreate and re-establish
total receptivity in our whole body,
we must first start to undertake
the re-education of the senses.

The senses must become the doors
by which all outer-form
can enter within us,
and impress us,
by reaching the centres of our attention
deep down in the skull-base,
left and right
below and behind the ears.

The Sense of Touch

All our senses depend on touch.
Our skin envelops the whole domain of our body.
The retinas are the sensitive inner skins of our eyes.
Inside our ears are the skins of our tympanums.
Deep in our mouth, the skin of the palate lets us tastc.
The skin inside the nose-wings, serves our sense of smell
near to our sense of taste.

Different vibrations of light and sound,
and also substances like air, carrying smells,
continually touch all these skins,
and enter our body causing sensations
passing along the threads of our nervous system.
When reaching our centres of attention
they create impressions.
All impressions blend at these centres.
But every sense has its own way of informing us
that we see, or hear, or feel, or smell, or taste.

All vibrations and substances
also enter through the pores of the skin
which cover our whole form.
There are places in our body
very sensitive, for instance,
to the touch of sound vibrations
such as the sockets in the pelvis
in which the heads of our thighbones move.

125

Here music awakes impressions in these sockets,
working directly on the legs.
Thus dance is born
without the brain interfering.

As the sockets of the armbones are intimately linked
to the sockets of the thighbones,
and the thighbones always respond
directly and intensely to sound;
there is in all these sockets
an inborn awareness of an inner rhythm.
The sockets of the thighbones are very near
to the centre of balance in our body,
which is the source of our life.
From there the breath of creative force
spreads through all the articulations.
It passes through the whole body and beyond.
Through the thighs, the knees, the ankles, feet and toes
in a downward direction,
and upwards through the sockets behind the armpits,
descending through the arms,
elbows, wrists and through the fingers.

The passing of life's breath through the whole form
is effortless, spontaneous and intense,
and co-ordinates all the different parts of the body
enabling it to move in outside space.

The Sense of Taste and Smell

In this book you have learned,
how on the very first day of life
of every human being,
the sense of taste and smell
is born,
when hands carry us
into our mother's bed,
we under-go the warmth
of our mother's body,
and find the precious food
nature has prepared for us.
Then the taste
of what is food and drink
gives us a new sensation
by its smell.
Later these natural functions weaken
through the mis-guided education
given to children.

On Sight

Images of forms in outside space,
fall on the retinas,
and travel along the nerves
which lead towards the centres of attention,
in the base of our skull-bone.

The images glide along the nerves
in a backward direction,
slightly sloping towards the centres of our attention,
to left and right
behind the ears.
This movement also reaches
the cavities of the ears.
Thus the impressions of hearing and seeing
can become united.

The movement of the images along the nerves
causes the sensation of sight.
The movement must not be disturbed,
when we try to focus upon the things we see,
by forcing a wrong movement in the opposite direction
from the centres of attention towards the retinas.
The nerves will then contract,
causing in the head,
and in the eyes and face
reactions,
upsetting the fine muscles around the eyes.
These tender muscles express
the subtle shades of emotion and thought.

If we learn to let the images
come home to the centres of our attention unmolested,
we will begin to see and become aware
not only of the forms we see in space,
but also of what is, and moves in them.

By and by, we will develop
another human capacity.
We will acquire
"insight".

Yesterday after Working with My Dear Lilian on "Sight"

Yesterday, after working with my dear Lilian on "sight",
I wrote a short poem on "hearing".
In the evening, David came to see me.
We were both very tired.
But so happy to be together
on the flow of the moments,
by which the advancing time — the future —
entered into our bodies and embraced us.
We were both listening in inner silence
to this passing of time,
as if a gentle breath
was stroking the lobes of our ears.
And my poem began to teach us a lesson.
David asked me to read the poem to him.
So I did.
At times he said, "Read those lines again".
I repeated them.
Suddenly I felt my inner dynamic vibrations
carrying the lines of the poem so intensely,
that for the first time, I could clearly explain to David,
how, what one says, can be carried
on the creative breath of life.

Pupils often beg me to explain this to them.
I realized then, that I can master a text so easily,
but I am not able to teach the pupils "How I do it".
It is not a "doing",
it is a "happening".
It happens when one lets creative breath carry one,
and allows it to vibrate in what one says.
Then every word will vibrate with the pure essence of its inner meaning.
Persons who listen, and look at another human being
in life or on the stage,
open their attention to the one who acts and speaks.
And so they enter into a state of inner interrogation.
The "performer" should therefore, before acting or speaking,
enter into the same state,
and thus establish the necessary inner at-onement
with their audience.

Please follow now what happened in me so consciously,
when I repeated the three lines of the poem to David.

The Three Lines

Here are the three lines
I repeated to David several times.
"From the cavities of the ears,
there is in a downward direction,
a direct link with the heels."

Preceding lines of the poem had awakened in David and me,
the strong sensation of the little wings of our ear lobes,
spreading and protecting the cavities of our ears.
During the evening, we had already established
the at-onement of being,
when we became aware
of the same Creative Presence
in both of us.

So when I said the simple words of the first line,
quite naturally the question was answered: "from where?".
And every time David asked:
"Will you tell me again 'from where?'".
I in myself, creating the same question each time he asked me,
just listened to how the question was answered within me:
"from where?"
And I said, "from the cavities of the ears",
there a movement begins.
And as an absolutely natural consequence,
there was the question about that movement:
"in what direction does it move?"
In the second line there is the answer
which happens inside of me,
and this must be spoken while it happens:
"in a downward direction".
Then quite naturally the question is born:
"Yes, what is there in that downward direction?"
There is the answer in the third line:
"a direct link with the heels".

So the one who speaks and acts,
and whose duty it is to move others
to take them on an inner journey,
he must *live with them their inner listening*,
their inner questioning.
He must join them, and live *their* inner life,
through the moments they have come
to be awakened, and to live an inner experience.
He must *be* with them,
and he can be with them,
by really intensely opening to them.

Asking oneself the questions born in those listening
awakes the dynamic vibrations,
which become visible and audible in a performer,
in a professional artist.
But also in an ordinary human being,
performing the role of his life
on the stage of this world.

The Poem on Hearing

The lobes of our ears are like small wings,
covering in a backward direction, the cavities in which
sounds are absorbed.
The outer shells of the ears of animals,
of primitive people, and of people belonging
to races in East and West, where traditions of
ancient civilizations are still alive,
stretch these lobes in a backward direction when they listen.
This movement helps to open wide the eyes.
It keeps the chords of the nerves free
from the retinas towards the centres of attention,
in order that sight and sound may co-ordinate.

From the cavities of the ears,
there is in a downward direction
a direct link with the heels.

In the bush, both for animals and primitive people,
it is of basic importance to be deeply attentive
to what they hear moving around.
They may not yet see,
but perhaps smell,
because their noses quiver.
Then they must at any moment be able
to take to their heels
at short notice.

The Natya Shastra Teaches

The Natya Shastra teaches that a performer on the stage
before composing his role in a personal way,
must already have composed his whole part in the play,
in a most intimate relationship with the audience.

Unconscious of such a principle,
already as a child I had this link with others,
without realizing exactly what took place within me.
This inborn "happening" developed in my life,
from my eighth year on,
when as a child, I appeared for the first time
on a stage, and thus became a "performer".
From then on, it stayed the basis
on which my work in the profession developed.
I always mastered it without any difficulty,
but I could never explain exactly,
how the sustaining activity of a presence was acting in me.

Yesterday, suddenly
whilst repeating a part of the poem to David,
I became clearly aware
of what happened inside my form.
And I felt the birth of dynamic vibrations.

I will now try to explain,
what in a most simple way happens,
when someone enters into communion
with one or more human beings,
and how this intimate relationship
establishes itself.

Prince Raden Mas Jodjana teaching meditation at the "Academy of Dramatic Art" in Amsterdam.

Jodjana said a Few Remarkable Things to Me

Jodjana said a few remarkable things to me
relating to his art of expression,
although he never liked to talk about this to others.

One day he said, "It all happens in me.
I feel *how* it happens,
because I am entirely present *when* it happens,
and I let it happen.
I do not *think* about it.
To feel something happening in you
is *not thinking* about it."

After a performance people always asked him:
"How do you do it?"
Very astonished he then asked:
"Were you not at my performance?"
Few people understood what he meant by this remark.

The people who collaborated with him knew
that there should be no discussion,
no talking during rehearsal.
There had to be absolute silence.
A rehearsal was listening towards within.
We had to create a consciousness of an inner state,
so that we too could partake in this process of feeling,
and letting it all happen within.

Jodjana when asked said:
"There is a way of thinking
about what happened within during a performance."
We have the possibility of reliving this past experience,
through going again within into that inner silence,
when that which took place in your inner space
happens again, and *tells itself to you.*
"This is the birth of creative thought."

Jodjana's art was founded
on four basic principles

He taught us,
that we must always feel
the ground underneath our feet,
whilst we are being active.
Thus we establish
our constant, intimate and balanced relationship
with the earth and the outside world.

133

Secondly we must create
a constant consciousness
of the two sides of our body.
Jodjana called that,
the basic life-consciousness
of symmetry.

Thirdly we must safeguard
the open mirroring quality of the brain,
by the spreading movement in our face:
nose-wings, eyelids, eyebrows, forehead,
and the implant of the hair around the forehead.
This can be practised, and prepares the concentration
of the two sides of the centres of attention,
above the support of the head
on the topmost vertebra.

The beginning of the fourth basic principle is,
that we should descend from the centres of attention
through our back towards the centre of gravity,
thus creating the relationship of the centres of attention
with the centre of gravity,
opening the path to pure concentration.
All our psychic and physical capacities
will then be free to serve
our creative expression.

Composition

Space which is inherent in all movement,
creates the pure expression of movement
when it can flow
through a perfectly relaxed and receptive human body.

Jodjana composed many dances
in this pure expression of movement.

The flow of life-breath through a body
creates two aspects of what is called pure dance.
Europeans know this and appreciate it
through the art of the classical ballet.

This flowing quality of space,
passing unhindered to all sides through the body,
creates the rhythmical quality in movement.
This is the first aspect of pure movement,
which awakes in man the ability to compose.

134

A composition should contain the *basic proportions*
of what is to be expressed.
This applies to any theme which moves us,
and stirs in us the necessity to create;
whether it is telling the story of an inner happening,
expressed in attitude, facial expressions and gestures,
using these movements, as sentences are formed with words.
Dances then become dance-pantomimes.
But if we express an inner state,
a deep consciousness of a state of being,
man's relationship to the cosmos or to his Creator –
all the invisible things which
from the beginning of creation
the Creator expressed in the creatures –
this can only be expressed by pure movement,
by the directions of movements in space,
on the flow of space through the whole body,
on the flow of time.
The composition then at the same time,
will have rhythmical quality, and reveal
the basic proportions of the composition.

All plays in Java are danced.
Jodjana when he was acting,
expressed the actions of the plays
on the rhythm of the flow of time,
in deepest relationship with space.
He thus revealed and manifested
by the *direction* of simple gestures and movements,
the inner meaning of the actions,
creating a new form of human relationship,
a direct *human* contact.

Improvisation

Jodjana pointed out, that performing
your own composition,
is quite a different art
to the art of composing a dance.
"Improvisation", he said, "demands a very rare gift
of recreating every time
a new presentation of a composition
on its basic proportions."
Whilst performing, there are many unforeseen demands
of very different natures.
Firstly the proportions of the given space
in which you have to perform.

135

Important also is the time of the day.
For instance, if you have to perform in a German theatre,
to dance or to act, between noon and 2.00 p.m. on a Sunday,
you cannot perform and meet the audience in the same way
as in an evening performance.
On a Sunday the audience being rested,
they are full of energy, and out to enjoy themselves.
At the evening performance, the people in the audience
who have been using their energy throughout the day,
are receptive, and open to the beauty and the humour
presented to them by the artists on the stage;
and are ready to live
the inner experiences of other human beings.

The artist must devote himself to the task
of awakening in the audience the deeper consciousness
of spiritual qualities.
The evening performances must be adapted
to this need of the audience.
The composition of the programme,
the execution of the dances or the acting,
must be built up on the principle
of the basic proportions of the composition,
and on the rhythm of the flow of time.

Jodjana, for instance, when he performed
the ceremony of the Rice Harvest,
suggested that he was carrying the basket with the rice seeds.
He would, by the directions of a few simple movements
make the audience believe that they saw the basket,
and that they saw the special knife
cutting every single tender stem of the rice plants.
All these "props" became visible by his simple language of movement,
never needing pantomimic gestures, or any other means
to indicate their outer forms.

The Natya Shastra

During a theatrical world congress in France,
I met a Hindu historian, Mr. Warma,
who was translating into the English language,
the oldest book on theatrical art
The Natya Shastra.

He read to the congress a very important paper,
on a part of this most interesting book.

In the East, the profession of performing on a stage
is a spiritual function.
Performers have a great responsibility,
and a very special definite task to fulfil.
They must awake in the public,
the consciousness of "what is other",
of what is around them in outside space.
They must open the mind and heart of the audience
to what is going on in other human beings,
to what is happening to the other person,
and to create in everybody present
the possibility of feeling fellowship.
They must break through the narrow confines
of personal interest,
and break down the will and tendency
to live at the cost of other beings,
harming and destroying them for personal benefit.

In the Natya Shastra, it is said,
that we, performers, before working our part in the play
in a personal way,
should first finish creating the role
in relation to the audience.

The theatrical people present
representing American and many European countries,
were absolutely at a loss what this could mean.
They assailed Mr. Warma with questions.
Mr. Warma had to stop his reading.
But he was unable to enter
into the Western way of discussion.

Having been trained for some years to perform Hindu plays,
I understood the teaching given in the Natya Shastra,
and listening to Mr. Warma's translation,
for the first time, I heard the exact terms
in which the Natya Shastra expresses this.
I was extremely happy
to hear the teaching *so well expressed*.

My husband and I had created a basis
allowing us to perform on this principle.
So I was deeply moved to discover
that we had really succeeded
in keeping such an ancient tradition alive,
in our work and teaching.

Some of our pupils present asked me
to try and explain the text just read by Mr. Warma.

But very loud and passionate discussion
had started between the many professional people.
They doubted that Mr. Warma
had translated the passage in the Natya Shastra
in the right way.
So they were not open to understand the meaning
of the basic teaching explained in the Natya Shastra.

In the East, especially among initiated adepts,
we abstain from such ways of discussion.
I joined Mr. Warma in silence.

Later the two of us had a very interesting meeting,
and we compared the application through the ages
of the basic teaching in the Natya Shastra
in Hindustan, and in Hindu-Javanese tradition.

In Hindustan, and in Java, our people
have now lost this basis.
I saw it still applied in Bali in a perfect way,
in a performance given by a group of peasant people.
For us this was a wonderful experience,
the balance between the constant dynamic vibration
in the moving grace of all movements,
carried and accompanied on the flow of time
by the sound of music and the throbbing drums.

I hope in this book,
I have been allowed and able
to explain in a simple and clear way
what the Natya Shastra tells us
to be the basic duty of performers;
in order to fulfil what is expected
from everyone who has chosen
the profession of appearing on a stage.

Preparation for Telling a Story

For telling a story,
giving a lecture,
reading a paper,
reciting a poem,
speaking on the stage,
or in daily life,
it is all the same
it needs the same preparation.

The content of the story,
the expression of the poem,
the theme of the lecture,
their essence and their substance
are all in you,
deep down in the centre
of your body.

There Creative Essence
starts to move –
this means, that the Creative Essence
deep down in your body,
creates movements
along the tender chords
of your nervous system.

Then all the physical substances,
air, muscles, bones and liquids,
begin to partake
in the process of expression.

Thus you can enter
into communion
with all other forms
in space around.
And communicate to them,
if you wish,
your impressions
and cxpcricnccs,
stored up in your centre of life,
in the centre of gravity,
ever at your disposal.

When You Go Out to Meet a Person or an Audience

When you go out to meet a person,
or an audience, to accomplish
a wish, an intention, or a necessity
born from within,
in this meeting you must be open.

As soon as you enter their presence,
you must receive them in your inner space.
You must listen to their questioning attention:
"What have you come to say to us,
or to do?"

Whatever you will say, or do,
must then be the answer to that question.

If you have come to perform a play,
or to recite a poem, or tell or read a story,
your whole performance should be
the continual answer to these questions.

This is the basis of all performing
on the stage, or in daily life.
Then life's dynamic force, will carry
your every word, gesture, and movement,
and will mirror in your facial expression,
and in your attitude.
You will live, be moved, and move
at-one with those you have come to meet.

The presence of Creative Essence – Space –
will link you not only with your audience,
but will open a cosmic relationship
between you and your audience.
After the meeting, or the performance,
everyone will go back to his daily life
in a different state of being.

Dynamic quality must become,
the basic quality of our expression.
The most perfected techniques
of expression, in movement and speech,
can help us to become good actors,
dancers, singers, and musicians.
But if we lack dynamic quality,
we may deserve appreciation,
but we will not be able
to really move others –
awake in them creative consciousness,
and help them to become free from the fetters
of their daily sorrows and preoccupations.

Without our dynamic expression fully alive,
we cannot awake in their bodies,
in their minds and hearts,
feeling which will open their attention
to what happens to others,
which is the most simple and spontaneous act of love.
We must enable them to feel,
space-functions working through all the substances of their bodies without constraint.

Dynamic value in expression is born
when creative breath bears all the movements of our bodies,

and translates itself into sound and words.
When our own breathing is sustained by the breath of life,
we will be able to master the language of movement,
as well as our vocal intonation.

On the stage, and in daily life,
we should, at every moment give full attention
to the inner state of those around us.
There will always be questions within them.

We, repeating these questions to ourselves,
give the answers in our acting,
and in all we do and say.

On the stage, and in daily life,
we should always stay aware
of the questioning state of those we are with.
Then ever new dynamic impulses
will bear our expressions,
in attitude, in facial expression,
in gestures, in movements and in words.

The Expressive Value of the Physical Form

Let us imagine that we have ordèred ballet-tights,
which will be especially made to fit us.
We have chosen a fine elastic fabric.
And a seamstress presents to us
the left stocking of the tights,
with plenty of the material above the stocking
to shape the pattern of the tights on the body.
We start to let our left foot
enter into the left foot of the stocking,
and feel how it enfolds our toes
and the sole of our feet,
its sides and instep
like a second skin.
We feel the springy material
totally enclosing our left foot.
We pull it over heel and ankle.
Further upwards it envelops our leg, the shin and calf,
the inside and outside of the leg.
We pull it over the knee, over the kneecap.
We feel it in the hollow of the knee-hole,
and then go on pulling it over our thigh,
enfolding the thigh tightly upwards to the groin.

141

The seamstress holds out to us the right-side of the stocking.
And our right foot starts to enter
the foot of the right stocking,
which enfolds our toes, our sole, our instep
and our heel and ankle.
We pull the stocking upwards.
It envelops our right leg, calf and shin.
We pull it over the right knee.

We feel how this articulation
can move freely, while we stay conscious
of its plastic value,
still sensing the second skin of the elastic material.
We go on, and let the material cover our thighbone upwards to the groin,
and in the back it stretches up to the buttock-muscles.

Let us for a moment intensely sense
and feel how both our legs are covered
by this second skin of the springy fabric,
while the seamstress joins the stockings back and front.
Then she pulls up the rest of the material.
In the back over the sacrum.
Over the hips, and in front up to the waist.
So now we feel the second skin
cover our pelvis.
And the seamstress pulls the fabric further upwards
and makes it tightly fit our body up to the armpits,
in the back towards the neck,
and in front around the arms over the chest.
Then on the shoulders she sews the shoulder seams.

There we stand in our ballet-tights.
And the seamstress offers us the left sleeve,
which our fingers enter one by one.
The hand follows, and around the wrist
we feel the second skin enfold the wrist-bone.
And we pull the sleeve over the forearm
up to the elbow, feeling the elastic second skin
tightly closing around this articulation.
Then we pull the sleeve up towards the shoulder
where kind helping hands
sew the sleeve on to the tights
covering our body:
first from the armpit upwards in the back,
then from the armpit upwards in front,
and the seamstress sews the shoulder seam
from the neck downwards to the upper armbone.
She offers us the right sleeve.
We enter it with our fingers,
each finger finding its own elastic covering.

142

Then hand, wrist, forearm, elbow, upper arm enter the sleeve
until it covers our whole arm.
The right sleeve is now sewn on to the tights covering our body:
first from the armpit in the back,
then from the front-side up to the shoulder.
There we stand, in our tightly fitting
elastic garment.

Then in the neck, a cap starts to cover
the back of our head, the skull, and over the sides of the head,
with holes cut out for the ears.
Then in front from below our throat, it covers
our chin and face, with holes for nose and eyes,
reaching over the forehead.

We now sit down just like a tailor sits on the floor.
And for a while we sense our body,
and get more and more at home in our body,
through feeling our skin.
It is suddenly announced that a sculptor
asks permission to have a look at us.
He is in need of a model with a consciousness
of the plastic value of his form in space.
We just sit and give no attention
for we do not know the sculptor who wishes
to study the result of the exercise.

We just go on trying to feel more and more
the totality of our form as onlookers see us.
As the sculptor moves around us,
he looks at us from different angles,
and we sitting there quietly
follow how he sees us
from these different points of view.
It is an intensely interesting experience,
while we work at the impression
on our inner consciousness,
of the plastic value of our form in space.
We can at the same time become
consciously aware of how
our form creates impressions on other human beings
in outside space.

Not so very long ago,
the great theatrical director Stanislawski,
spent a fortune building a theatre in Moscow,
with many expensive installations
to help actors attain the consciousness
of how their form impressed their audience.
You can find how Stanislawski taught this in a book,

which he wrote to the artists in his group.
The title of the book is "An Actor Prepares".
Stanislawski knew this consciousness could be obtained.
And he did not spare expense to awaken it
in the members of his theatrical group.
He clad the actor in the embrace of a spotlight,
the rest of the stage being pitch dark.
The actor started to feel the embracing light
tightly enfolding his skin.
And as the light was diffused, he had to try
to keep this sensation alive.

Now we offer here this simple exercise of the tights,
in order that everybody may obtain
this feeling, and consciousness of the plastic value
of the body.
And not only for those who perform in public, on a stage,
but also those, who in daily life
care to express their inner attitude by their visible form.

Part VI: The Grammar

The Art of Intonation

Expressing ourselves by the sound of words,
the basic value of all the Arts
should be present in our intonation.

Sentences should be built
according to the proportions of architecture.
Words should be moulded like a sculptor's hand moulds clay.
The sound must be carried on the breath like music,
and on an inner rhythm on which dance is born.
And in our voice, the vibrations of sound will create
the tone the painter expresses in lines and colours.

Learning the Art of Intonation

To be able to master
the directions of the movements
of words,
in order to create intonation,
you must study language anew.

Because one must become clearly aware
of the directions of these movements,
when expressing the meaning of words.
We shall create a new grammar of language,
from which we can learn
all languages on the same basis.
We shall gratefully use the order
of the established grammars,
and on this well-known basis,
teach the creative inner movements
which brought the words to life.

Life's vibration in words,
expresses itself in direction.
Direction is space working in movement.

Before We Learn to Speak in Life

Before we learn to speak in life
we express ourselves in movement.
Then, we can only express ourselves
by sounds, caused by sensation.
We cry, we laugh,
we sigh, we make noises
like the animals.
Because the brain of infants
only mirrors the sensations
which slowly become feelings.

This process develops the mirroring quality in the brain.
The brain-mirror begins to reflect.
By a long evolution in the primates
these processes
led to the creation of a new species.
The creatures belonging to that new species
live in upright position.
We call that creature – Man.
Evolution demands that man
becomes a human being
and develops human qualities.
This process of evolution
works in every infant born on earth,
by developing the mirroring quality in the brain.

At first the brain mirrors vague moving images,
the same happens in the brain of animals,
by and by the pictures become clearer.
The pictures never stop moving.
Our dreams are sometimes like silent moving pictures.
The child does not think, it reflects.
This means the brain reflects
what is happening in the child.
But the French verb "réfléchir"
suggests that becoming conscious of this happening,
the child starts to master this process
and becomes a "doer".

At the same time an effort to name the moving images
begins to develop a new activity in the brain.
The mounting movement in the back
creating the images is accompanied
by this other mounting movement
developing in the back:
the capacity to think.

Imagining and thinking should stay creative,
but by wrong education,
thinking has become a process
of trying to bring the moving images to a halt.
Then the brain begins to lose its mirroring quality.
It starts to grab and to hold,
and to imprison the images in fixed pictures
in the mind.
These mind-pictures uproot thoughts
from the living soil of creative intelligence,
and eradicate the intimate co-ordination of spirit and soul,
of mind and feeling,
of thought and image.
Life in the brain becomes obtuse,
and we start to live on abstractions,
separated from the source of life,
obstructing the breath of space
in our form, and in the substances of our body.

Thereby we have lost the capacity
to express ourselves on life's vibration in sound,
and in what we say.
There no longer exists anywhere in the world a teaching
in the art of intonation.
We learn to speak, to declaim
by firing the pitch of the voice,
by changing the speed of our enunciation
on the basis of a metronome.
Feeling becomes pathos,
which degenerates the melodious quality of the voice,
the inner rhythm,
and kills the simple, true and beautiful meaning of words.

In a following poem,
we will try to introduce
a mode of sound-expression,
which may open the possibility
of reviving this wonderful art of intonation,
which will lead us into the world of the beauty
of language.

Ill-use of words, can never corrupt
the working of the soul in words.
The mystery of this perfection of human speech
should one day reveal itself again
in the intonation in every human voice.

The Grammar

When we use words to communicate with those around us,
the consciousness of our relationship to outside space
is of great importance.

When we use NOUNS, that is the naming of things,
we must place these things where they should be in space around us.
If the things referred to "are moving",
this is indicated by the use of VERBS.
Our attention should absorb the movements and directions of these VERBS.

We find three regions in which we must be able
to master this placing of words, and the movement of VERBS.
There is the space behind us.
There is the space within, and just around us,
and space in front of us.
So when we use NOUNS naming things which belong to the past,
also expressions indicating the past,
as for instance the words:
"This morning": "Yesterday": "Last year";
or expressions like:
"Long ago"; "In the past century".
While speaking these words,
we should open our attention
towards the region behind our back,
and move about in that space.
Also, the same applies when we use the past tense of a VERB,
for instance:
"I was"; "They thought"; "It happened".

If we speak about the present,
using the words: "In this moment",
or name for instance
the chair in which we sit,
or say: "We are", "You see", "He thinks",
We must be there,
with our attention
very present and alive.

The third region in space lies in front of us.
From there, the movement of our future tasks
enters without ceasing into our inner space.
And towards that region of space our attention opens
ready to accept these tasks,
and prepares us to respond.

150

When we speak about the future,
we use simple terms like:
"Tomorrow", "Later", "Maybe",
and we use the future tense of VERBS:
"I shall try", "They will decide", "We should".
Thus when our attention opens
towards that region in front of us,
the creation of our relationship
towards that region of space
will sound in the intonation of our voice.

Nouns

Nouns name forms.
Before mentioning these forms,
we should join in the interrogative state
of the people present.
The answer that I give to these questions
awakes in me the same state of interrogation
in those around us.
It also awakes the dynamic vibrations
which will carry the answer.

We name the noun on a movement,
directing what we name
to where we wish to place it in outside space.
Thus the inner meaning of the noun
will become visible,
taking form in the minds of those who listen.
Because you will have created the form
in a clearly indicated place in outside space.
You can even make the form more visible,
giving it relationship to other forms you have placed.

When pronouncing a noun
you must always place it clearly in space.

There are nouns which do not name things,
they name conditions, qualities, feelings,
like: "fatigue", "goodness", "alertness".
Pronouncing these nouns we depend
on our inborn understanding of adjectives.
We must *feel* the condition of "being tired",
or feel the state of "goodness",
or when we feel "alert".

We call these nouns: "Adjectival Nouns."

Adjectives

What I have just told you regarding "Nouns",
which do not name things,
has introduced what you must know
about adjectives.

Adjectives will always be used
in connection with nouns.
Adverbs ask for the same movement
in connection with verbs.

These inner feelings and inner states
express themselves mostly
in the changing of facial expression.
But also in attitudes and gestures.
They are spontaneous movements
which are improvised within us,
and in a natural way accompany our words.
These movements become visible
before we pronounce what we are going to say,
and prepare those who are listening.

Learning the art of intonation,
we give up "doing" the movements,
mechanically executing gestures like a machine.

Verbs

Verbs are nearly always actions.
Actions demand inner and outer movements.
Inner movements are when we think,
imagine, hope, plan, believe, decide.
Outer movements continue these innner movements
along the nerves,
and visibly show that we see, hear, feel,
absorb and assimilate.

We also express ourselves in such actions
as walking, writing,
or moving different parts of our body.
All these movements become visible in outside space,
and express themselves by their directions.
Direction reveals the soul of a word in expression.
And you know already
that space is the only Creative, Expressive Essence.

152

So you are going to learn language anew,
first of all your own language,
by discovering the inborn direction of words.

The verb "to go" starts from our centre of gravity,
and is a movement in forward direction in space.
When you use this verb "to go"
you should express this movement in a forward direction
by bouncing from the backward supports of your body.
Whenever you use the verb "to go",
in the expressions: "I go", "they go", "it goes" etc,
you must always express
this same bouncing movement in a forward direction,
because you indicate in your expression – "the going".

You also have to show whether
the movement happens in the past, in the present,
or if it will happen in the future.
The personal pronouns indicate
from where the movement starts.

Here follow a series of verbs.
We will tell you the basic directions of their movements,
showing the inner meaning of these verbs.
Then you will be able to find
the basic direction of every verb you use.

The verb "to come" is always a movement
from somewhere in space moving towards you.
Now you know the basic movement of verbs never change.
If you say: "I come", "they come",
or use the imperative: "Come!"
The starting point of the movement will be different.
But the verb "to come"
no matter from where it starts,
must always move towards you.
When you say: "I come",
begin to spread your body from its centre
as you pronounce the personal pronoun "I",
and on saying "come",
you move back to your centre.

The verb "to see",
starts from the retinas of the eyes, inwards,
and moves along the optic nerves
backward-downward towards the centres of attention.

"To say", "to speak", "to whisper",
"to kiss", "to pout",

153

all these verbs play on the lips,
and from there are thrown back to the throat wall.

The verbs "to think", "to hope", "to imagine", "to consider",
are all movements which mount by themselves
in the back towards the brain,
and there, move through the brain-cells,
until you have prepared the change
of the basic direction of the next word.

Preparing the transitions of these changes of directions,
you will nearly always find punctuation marks,
such as a comma.
There should never be a break
in the movements of these transitions.

There are verbs which do not express a movement.
They do not have a basic direction.
They need a complement, a noun or an adjective
which refers to the subject of the phrase.
Therefore the noun or adjective is
in the same case as the subject.

If I say: "I am tired",
or tell people "who I am, or what is my profession",
I first start to detach myself from my centre of gravity
when I pronounce the verb "am",
but on pronouncing the noun or adjective
I come back to my centre.

Pupils like to study these verbs,
as the movement
helps them to master the technique
of throwing back the consonants
towards the backwall of the throat.
This prevents them from pushing the words
outwards into space.

Personal Pronouns

Before we start on the pronouns,
I must state once more,
that all we say or do
must be a spontaneous, creative expression
of a happening in our inner space.

A happening is a space movement
in this inner space.
We must be moved.
These innner movements perform themselves.

We must abstain
from any planning, and *doing* movements
according to fixed images and thoughts
in our brain.
We must only feel and undergo
the inner movements.
Let them happen,
then our whole form and body
will become the instrument
in which these spontaneous, creative expressions
take place.

The personal pronouns are spoken on a movement
from the centre of balance
emanating to all sides throughout the body.

We have told you
that the art of intonation
is the art of creating an inner choreography
carrying the creative soul of words
on the flow of time.
It is an art —
the inner performing of a dance.
It asks the tremendous mastering of inner time
and for an enormous variety of creative expression.
If once you understand
how to practise the basis of this art,
you can sometimes master it immediately.
You must practise it
by reading a text in this way,
using the basis of understanding
and of direct awareness,
building up all the changes of direction
revealing the creative value
of the composition of the text.

We can start developing this gift
with the simple pronoun "I",
realizing its infinite shades of expression.
The pronoun "I" may translate itself
in many different varieties of expression.
Someone may choose you to fulfill an action.
You may feel honoured, amazed, flattered,
or unwilling or annoyed,

by simply announcing your inner state
on the vibrations of your emotions,
when you pronounce the word "I".
When the sound of the word is no longer audible
the working in space of its inner vibrations
will continue as long as you keep it alive.

On this principle, all the other personal pronouns
can be expressed.
The pronoun "We" has a different starting point
according to whether there are other people present.
By a uniting movement,
one awakes in one's inner being
this unity,
and then pronounces: "We."

"You", "He", "She", "It", "They".
All these personal pronouns only differ
according to the actual visible presence
which we must very clearly indicate in a place
in space around,
or indicate very clearly in backward space
the place we have chosen.

Relative Pronouns

The relative pronoun begins a part of a sentence
telling about the special relationship
to a person, or to a thing mentioned
in the previous part of the sentence.
There is always a comma
before the relative pronoun.
Because of this puntuation mark
a moment of silence is created.
Then going back to the last word before the comma
we make a new beginning of the relative sentence.
The relative pronoun links the two parts
of the main clause.

Demonstrative Pronouns

The demonstrative pronoun is also indicating clearly,
either a thing which is present in space around
or somewhere in space *we choose*.
It is pronounced on exactly the same principle
underlying all pronouns.

156

Possessive Pronouns

Possessive pronouns: "My", "Your",
"His", "Her", "Our", "Their", "Its",
all start on the same principle,
either starting from a visible object seen by everyone,
or by our clear indication
by *suggesting* an exactly chosen indicated place.

The Indefinite Article

The indefinite article has an impersonal meaning.
For intance, it expresses the difference
between: "the man" or "a man".
"A man", the starting point
is somewhere in space around us,
which refers to any man, in any place.
While "the man", denotes a specific person
in a specific place.

Counting

When numbering in counting
1, 2, 3, onwards,
we sometimes accompany the counting
with a gesture,
like counting on our fingers.

When we make a noun from a number
like the "first", or "second",
we can express our personal feelings
about the value of that number.
When we use a numeral as a noun
up to the number 10,
we are indicating a part of a certain number.
When we count up to 10,
we can count silently,
and on reaching the chosen number
give a very special delicate accent
to that number.

157

Prepositions

Then there are the prepositions
which are very important.
They clearly indicate a relationship
between two different objects in space,
because they always announce
a relationship of direction.
The value of the meaning of this relationship
in our inner being,
will influence the colour, and the tone
of the pronunciation of the word.

Conjunctions

We end with the conjunctions –
but they are not difficult to express,
and are constantly used in all texts.

Firstly there are the conjunctions
"and" and "or".
For instance: "The ball *and* the top."
"The ball and the top", must be placed carefully
in two different places
linked with the conjunction
"and",
which may be accompanied by a gesture.

The conjunction "or",
necessitates the same placing,
but expresses that there is a choice to make –
"this *or* that".
"This" must be visible and audibly expressed.

Another conjunction "but",
asks from those who listen
a new awakening of their attention.

If I use "while", "whilst",
I state that something
is taking place at the same time
which shows quite a different inner attitude.

Conjunctions must very especially awaken
a deeper understanding
of what is going to be said.
The consequence is,

158

that when speaking the words of a text
we must be emotionally alive,
creating the necessity of our being moved
while we speak.
By feeling the inner meaning of the word
we can awake inner feeling in those who listen.

Raden Ayou Jodjana and Raden Mas Jodjana in the garden of the "Berthe Trumpe Tanzschule" Berlin 1938, planning a performance. Raden Ayou Jodjana was Director of the "Berthe Trumpe Tanzschule".

Raden Ayou Jodjana singing Hindu songs.

Raden Ayou Jodjana playing the Tamboorah.

Raden Mas Jodjana and Raden Ayou Jodjana and Roumahlaiselan at home in their flat in the Valerius-straat in Amsterdam after a performance.

Parvati Jodjana 12 years old.

Bhimo Jodjana 3 years old.

Prince Raden Mas Jodjana as professor at the "Academy of Dramatic Art" in Amsterdam.

Raden Mas Jodjana in the dance "Hiranyakashipu" – The Evil King.

Prince Raden Mas Jodjana as "Shiva".

Roumahlaiselan in the dance "The Downfall of the King".

Raden Mas Jodjana and Roumahlaiselan backstage in the dressing room of the Volksbühne Theater, Berlin.

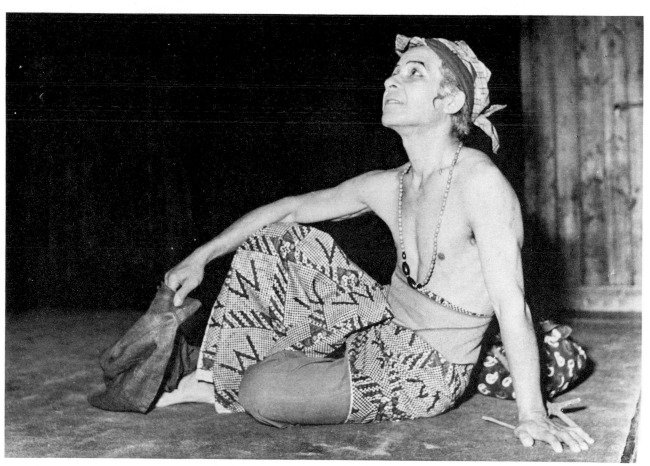

Roumahlaiselan in "The Stone Cutter".

Prince Raden Mas Jodjana as "Krishna".

Raden Mas Jodjana as "Ardjuna".

*Raden Mas Jodjana in the dance "Måyå-Måyå"
Dance of the Green Dusk.*

*Raden Mas Jodjana in the dance "Tjantrik" — The
Young Hermit.*

*Raden Mas Jodjana in the dance "Hamudji" — Prayer
without Words.*

Prince Raden Mas Jodjana.

Part VII: Autobiography

One day in London I Went to a Concert

One day in London I went to a concert,
given by Hindu musicians
at the Royal Asiatic Society.
A great Hindu singer, Hazrat Inayat Khan,
was accompanied on string instruments
the dilruba and sitar,
played by Mohammed Ali, his cousin,
and Mushraff, his youngest brother.
Maheboob Khan played the tabla, the Hindu drums.

I myself, a young singer
from early childhood on, had lived
through many extraordinary experiences.
My parents told me that
as a baby I would sit enraptured,
my little finger lifted
intensely listening.
My baby hands starting to move
on my little table,
as on the keys of a piano.
And later with two sticks
I was playing the violin,
with the same enraptured expression.

In childhood and girlhood, going to rehearsals
of the orchestra in The Hague,
created by Viotta, who married my mother's cousin;
I listened to the music played
by many great artists –
like Pablo Casals, Hubermann,
Pugno, Lucien Capet
and the Casadessus.

My parents were approached by these musicians,
telling them that they were inspired
by my way of listening.
I myself, had no idea what this meant.
But before the First World War,
I accompanied the Capet Quartet
and Mengelberg's Orchestra on tour
as a "mascot".

As a child I passed much time
in the studios of great painters.

They also liked me to be there
and used me as a model.
And later I often hung the pictures
for their exhibitions.
It was all so natural to me,
I never felt it as something out of the ordinary.

I seriously decided to work very hard
to become an artist myself.
I gave concerts and performances.
But the special gift to inspire others
turned my life into the path
along which I had to develop –
to teach how to act creatively.

So I was called to serve.
First the genius of Inayat Khan,
and then my Javanese husband,
Raden Mas Jodjana.

Hazrat Inayat Khan was Sent by His Guru from India to the West

Hazrat Inayat Khan was sent by his Guru,
from India to the West,
to bring a gentle message of love and humility
to Western people.
Inayat Khan was a great musician, a singer, a bard.
And he was sent to bring the message by song,
and by the poetry of the great Sufi Masters.

Many Western people came
and listened to the songs sung by Inayat Khan,
accompanied on his sacred instrument, the vina.
Many of them could not understand these songs
not being accustomed to listen
to the Creative Presence.
And they silenced their Master.

Inayat Khan, my Guru, foretold my future meeting
with another being
with whom I was to enter
the path of destiny.
He told me exactly the sign that would be given
to me, and to that other human being.
It was a symbol of seven crowns with seven stars.

164

We met, were united and married;
and were guided by the same inner Presence,
together bringing the message,
not in word, not in music
but in pure movement.
Raden Mas Jodjana, my husband, had come from Java
to Europe with a mission.
It was the same message as Inayat Khan's.
Not given out by music
but in the language of pure movement.

By performing on the stages all through Europe,
he made many Westerners aware,
that the human being can express himself
in a simple, intense and beautiful way
by movement.
With a simple gesture, by turning the head,
just lifting a finger,
or moving through space.
Jodjana revealed and manifested
that man can develop the inner consciousness
of creative intelligence,
and from within, spread knowledge
by creative expression in movement.

It was in Ladbroke Road in London
that I came to Inayat Khan for the First Music Lesson

It was in Ladbroke Road in London
that I came to Inayat Khan for the first music lesson.
I entered the room with a book and pencil.
He asked me why I brought that book and pencil.
And when I said that I wished to take notes
of all he was going to teach me,
he seemed amazed and said:
"Have you not received the gift of memory?
Learn to listen well to all I am going to teach you.
Let it enter and impress you.
Then you will forget to 'remember'.
What will be forever stored in your memory
must for some time stay in oblivion,
until it can serve you in creative expression
at a certain moment.
Only what you need to remember in the moment
should mount in the consciousness of the brain.
Never come to me with a book and pencil.

165

One should not use crutches on the path to Being.
When you are with me, dive deep within yourself.
Try to become at-one with that all-pervading,
Infinite Being.
That you may live to know the end of separation."

He let me leave the room to put away the book and pencil.
Coming back I sat down prepared to listen
as he asked me to do.
He sang to me, and opened that wonderful world of silence,
which I had entered into for the first time
when I heard him sing in the concert he gave
at the Royal Asiatic Society in London.
This was just before the First World War
broke out.

He sang.
It must have been for quite a long time.
In the world of silence one lives timelessly.
When he had finished he said to me:
"Now it is your turn."
By my vows I was not allowed to put a question
nor to hesitate to obey an order.
I became suddenly very uncertain
having to improvise after his singing
in the same rag, on the same theme
and in the same tal, or rhythm.
He had not yet taught me the patterns
of the ragas and raghinis.
Previously when we lived
in Addison Road, he made me sing the prayers
I had heard sung by him and his musicians.
Now in the lesson starting to improvise in a rag,
I became conscious of my incapacity
to live up to the task.

When I finished there was a long silence.
Then he said: "I see that you can still enormously develop
the quality of your memory,
you may remember that this is 'Pilu'."
He did not explain what Pilu meant.
A Guru does not give explanations.
Knowledge should come from within.
Knowledge is born from the depth of being.
Yogi's teach their adepts by symbolic postures
expressing an inner condition.
Most of these masters have lived in caves,
where adepts go to them.

I had accepted to stay in the relative world,
and there to live in the cave of my own body.
Therefore no longer to put questions,
not to speak about inner experiences, or an inner state,
to obey orders immediately without hesitation or discussion.
Not helped by a withdrawal from the outside world,
it was often a very steep descent for me into the inner self.
Many times I felt as though I were dropping into an abyss.
This should lead to an inner condition, enabling one
to perform a very special task in the relative world.

Yogis in the caves of the Himalayas
attaining God-consciousness,
mostly stay united with the Divine Presence
and do not return to the relative world.
Staying in this world in order to fulfil special tasks,
extreme humility must be attained
to become able to serve others –
the living and the dead.
It demands a never-ending process
of renouncing the self,
living the life of a recluse,
yet sharing with others all vicissitudes
of life in this world.
The life of Inayat Khan was such a life.

Once Discouraged by the Lack of Results in My Lessons

Once discouraged by the lack of results in my lessons,
I ceased straining my ears.
I just sat listening to my master's sweet voice singing,
no longer trying to rivet my attention
in order to capture information
about the structure of the songs.
I just listened to the music
and entered the marvellous state of inner silence.
Suddenly I recognized an inner atmosphere
I had experienced before.
And when Inayat Khan asked me:
"Kurshid, what expresses this song?"
I answered: "Pilu."
He smiled, and I knew that at last I had learned to listen,
to listen with the whole body.

One hears with the ear!

From then on I began to know the ragas and raghinis,
to know how to sing and to improvise.

167

I became able to absorb sound and rhythm
at the same time.
I began to feel and follow, deep down in my body
the pulsation of time.
I could follow the melodic line of the songs
against the background of the accompaniment
by the string instruments – vina, dilruba and sitar;
or the soft humming of the musicians,
feeling the pulsation in time
in the sound pictures.

This formed a basis for the number of measured moments
of the tal, the rhythm.
I then started to work with Maheboob,
who played the tabla, the two Hindu drums.

The hearing capacity of the human ear
gives us the possibility of registering sounds and noises.
While the incoming sound vibrations run along
the nervous chords,
the brain capacities should only register the incoming sensations
and let them pass unmolested
to the centres of attention left and right,
deep in the base of the skull.
And then let them descend inside the back
to the bottom of the pelvis.
So the intellectual capacities of the brain should not grasp
at incoming impressions,
and deal with them according to fixed standards.

Sound vibrations do not only touch the skin inside the ears.
In a very special way they are absorbed
by the whole body through the skin.
They enter into the sockets, into the very cavities,
in which the heads and necks of our thighbones
are supported.
Thus movements of legs and feet start from there spontaneously,
and dance is born.
In these sockets all sounds are captured
and work directly on the heads of the thighbones,
making legs and feet obey immediately.
Spontaneous movement is only possible
when not ordered by the brain.
If there is an explosion, the threatening noise
will cause the legs to run away from danger.
If there is music, the legs and feet will begin
to move on the rhythm of the music and will dance.

Let us leave to the ears and brain
the task of obtaining knowledge
of what caused the explosion,
or what piece of music made us dance.

The very successful Hindu, Japanese and other Eastern masters,
now creating many of to-day's world movements,
owe their success to a very great extent
to a few great masters, who, in the beginning of this century
opened for those who are teaching now,
the minds of Europeans and American people.
The few great masters attracted followers by their extreme humility,
their noble human conduct, and patient suffering.

Gandhi, Inayat Khan, and Raden Mas Jodjana;
we, who witnessed their tragic lives, hope
that sometimes the successful creators
of different methods of meditation today,
will gratefully remember these pioneers,
who taught us, on the basis of the old traditions —
creative expression —
and initiated us into the working of creative intelligence.
They taught us Transcendental Meditation,
in order to arrive at a state of being,
in which we could join them
and enter into the service of the Creative Presence,
uniting us with all other form in the Universe.

Inayat Khan Initiated Me before there was a Sufi Order

Inayat Khan initiated me when we lived in Addison Road
before there was a Sufi Order.
His brothers, his cousin and his wife
were then the only murids.
Later in Ladbroke Road he asked me not to join
the Sufi Order.
He ordered me to teach Western music to his musicians,
thus enabling Mohammed Ali to become a very wonderful singer,
and also later to prepare concerts in the Lecture Hall
of the Sufi Centre in Ladbroke Road.
He wrote plays to be performed by us.
He sang duets with me,
and presented me at the Queen's Hall, to the English public.

169

In this way Inayat Khan stayed true to his own vow —
by singing in his unique sweet way,
opening for those who could listen
the path into the inner world
to meet the Divine Presence within.
And so to learn to serve the Presence silently
in full acceptance of one's destiny,
meeting all beings as expressions of the same Presence.

In meditation I learned to enter within inner space,
into inner silence,
and began to become aware of the inner interrogative state.
I started to know how to serve, what to do,
how to obey
without the mind interfering,
questioning or discussing.
Just the clear inner awareness of what to do in the moment.

It was not easy as I had never learnt before
to accept with the whole body, mind and soul
this inner guidance.
Never before had I known that the body can
and should become wholly receptive.
Therefore I had to teach the body to open to all sides
its nervous system, the brain included,
and to relax the whole muscular structure.
The mind then stays receptive.
The centres of attention absorb impressions
and let them descend to the source of life.

Inayat Khan did not tell and explain all this to me,
and no questions were allowed.
But the questions were there,
and the mind had to be silenced.
Downwards the questions went, and created by and by
the inner interrogative state.
Taking the habit of listening towards within,
at last one discovers
that the inner questions receive their true answer,
awakening awareness
of what to do or not to do,
of what to say or not to say
in the moment.

From the centre of gravity,
from the centre of balance and being,
inspirations and ideas,
inner awareness and intuition
will be born, and create intentions
to act and to speak,

170

or not to move and keep silent.
In this way Inayat Khan was directing me
to the deepest consciousness of life.
But I struggled a long time in utter darkness.
It brought me to the last choice,
leading me on the inner path, backward-downward,
never again to change direction.

In this way one learns,
that there is only one way to go for our attention.
And its direction we should know —
backward-downward.

I Witnessed Different People Beginning to Frequent Inayat Khan's House

I witnessed different people beginning to frequent
Inayat Khan's house.
Not in search of a Sufi message,
but eager to introduce into their lives
something very attractive by its beauty,
and by its unique artistic expression.
They tried to create a closed circle of people
under the gentle guidance of a great artist,
beginning to be known in Europe for his art.
Inayat Khan was the head of a family group
stranded in London when the First World War broke out,
without any means of a livelihood.
The group of adepts in London began to lay down
restraining rules for those becoming members of their circle.
They fixed a contribution, imposing the responsibility
of paying for housing the centre,
sheltering Inayat Khan's family,
and assuring their livelihood.

Inayat Khan never created the Sufi Order in London.
He accepted the offer of the group of people
who made the proposal.
He was then told by the board of the circle
to give lectures and lessons,
as they wished to know more
about the still unknown secrets of Hindu Yoga.
They wanted him to teach by word
and explain clearly what it was all about.

Shortly before leaving Addison Road,
the family and I began to listen to Inayat Khan
during the services of music in the evenings,

171

when he started to explain
many truths not previously taught in the English language.
Later in Ladbroke Road I was often astonished
and sometimes shocked,
how people reacted when Inayat began
his first teaching by word.
This made him come to the conclusion
that Western people could never be pupils or adepts,
as they always knew better!
There were a few exceptions.
Like Miss Goodenough
whom Inayat always saw in private.

I think she helped the family to live.
She must have taken the vow of silence.
She never mixed with the family,
nor did she speak with the other murids.
Inayat Khan seemed to trust her more than anybody else
outside the family.
I saw her frequently and liked her.
She was discreet, and treated me as a member
of Inayat's family.

In the Intimate Circle of Inayat's Family, We Formed the First Group in England of Initiated Adepts

In the intimate circle of Inayat Khan's family in Addison Road,
we formed the first group in England
of initiated adepts.
Begam, his young wife, and I were the only women
in this circle.
Inayat Khan taught us all to master emotional states
causing reactions in conduct and expression.
And he submitted all of us to severe tests.
Maheboob was the most advanced murid.
He showed me the way to listen towards within
for the answer to the problems we met in daily life.
Mohammed Ali, a man of deep passions,
was very severe with himself and with others.
Mushraff never arrived at mastering his emotions.
Inayat was very severe with him.
I knew Mushraff to the very last,
always reacting in an emotional way.
Crying and sobbing and causing painful scenes,
having no inner understanding of Western people,
not even of his own people in their reactions
to Western adepts.

172

He came to the West too young, and was never able to cope
with the experience of intimate contact
with a people so different from his own.

After moving to Ladbroke Road,
we stopped leading a family life.
The whole family lost their original happy attitude
towards the outside world.
They were kind but aloof in their contacts with people.
Thus our group in Ladbroke Road became isolated.
Miss Goodenough in silence, was ever present
although never entered the family circle,
nor any other part of the house
then reserved for members of the Sufi Order.

Even Miss Williams the secretary, living in the same house
did not join us in private life.
She, though meaning to be humble,
could not master her emotional reactions.
She suffered much, being neither appreciated
by members of the Sufi Order, who made her life hard,
nor by the family silently witnessing her sufferings
and her reactions.
I understood her well.

Bound by vows,
Living in the cave of my body,
suffering stayed subdued.
So I lived silently united
with Miss Goodenough and Miss Williams.
The other murids giving me little attention
treated me as the servant of the family.
Inayat Khan often left the house in order
to avoid meeting the always intruding murids.
He made me answer the door.
I trained myself to meet them
understanding their Western outlook and conduct.

In Ladbroke Road no one ever came to the top floor
where the family wished its privacy to be respected.
Inayat lived in the front room with his wife and child.
The three "boys" stayed in the back room
with a view on the garden.
I had to clean the rooms, took out the child,
as Begam no longer went out in the world.
She started to live in purdah.
The "boys" never entered the front room.
I was the only person to serve Inayat and his wife in their room.

There was often a sad atmosphere.

173

Begam whom I had known young and smiling in Addison Road,
changed entirely living in the centre of the Sufi Order.
She lost her radiance
and avoided contact with the Western adepts.
It was in Holland in the house of Mrs. Van Goens,
whose daughter Maheboob was to later marry,
that I saw Begam leading a family life again,
just as in Addison Road.

In Ladbroke Road the midday meal was taken
by Inayat Khan, Maheboob, and Mohammed Ali in the basement,
where I used to join them.
Inayat begged me not to become a member of the Sufi Order.
He wished to lead me, according to the wish of his Guru,
in the path of the Sufi way of life.
I am most indebted to him.
He prepared me to be able to bring with my husband
the same Sufi message,
expressed in movement
but in the Hindu-Javanese idiom.

As Inayat Khan Asked Me not to Join the Sufi Order

As Inayat Khan asked me not to join the Sufi Order,
but desired to lead me according to the wish of his Guru
in the path of the Sufi way of life,
where no explanations were given,
no questions were allowed.
Discussion, according to Inayat Khan
was postponement of application.
I had to take the vow of immediate obedience.
I was directed towards within
by transcendental meditation.
I had to live in space inside the body.
In the dark.
This was necessary to awake, accept and create
the inner interrogative state.
Later joining my husband in the circle of Javanese Sufis,
the esoteric "Wayang" play of "Bhimo",
gave me a clear insight
into Inayat Khan's own initiation by his Guru,
and the teaching he gave to me.

Within the family circle of Inayat Khan there was no "talk".
Silence was a very expressive and necessary state
in order to listen towards within,
and to cultivate inner silence.

174

All sound expression was in music.
Inayat Khan asked me to help
to keep sound-expression in music
alive in Ladbroke Road.
As soon as the Sufi Order was established there
very disturbing talk was heard.
It was then that Inayat Khan
began to write plays, and the "boys" and I performed in them.
Inayat Khan checked my inner progress severely,
purposely causing distressing, unforeseen
and very trying situations.
I will give an example.

Once I was offered a unique chance,
and invited to make my London debut
at Leighton House in Holland Park.
A European concert-hall of great repute.
I had introduced Inayat Khan
into the circle of great artists
who managed the hall.
Inayat ordered the "boys" to accompany me
in the performance.
The day before the performance I went to Ladbroke Road
for a last rehearsal.
I did not know that Inayat had told the boys
to play the accompaniment out of tune,
and to upset the rhythmic structure of the songs.
I made tremendous efforts and spent hours
trying to adjust myself to accept the strain.
Going home I became very distressed,
not knowing how they would play in the performance.
They played marvellously well in the twilight concert
the next day.
The performance was a great success.

Another time Inayat Khan was presenting me
at the Queen's Hall to the English public.
He was singing duets with me.
Suddenly during the perfomance he began to sing
my small solo part.
My knees started to tremble.
I tried to save the situation by repeating
words and melody in a humble, questioning expression,
as if I asked him: "Do you now wish me to sing this?
Do I sing it in the way it should be sung?"
This was, so to say, a true interpretation
of the situation.
In moments of utter distraction,
Inayat Khan seeing my efforts to master the situation
laughed heartily, as if he enjoyed
exposing me to public shame.

In a quite incomprehensible way,
I always felt an astounding inner help
in these vexing moments.
And these experiences formed the basis of a rare joy,
when once after singing a geaal,
I saw him very moved.
He said: "You will go far on this long Path."

The Last Song of Inayat Khan

Before you judge my actions
Lord, I pray you will forgive.
Before my heart has broken,
Will you help my soul to live?
Before my eyes are covered,
Will you let me see your face?
Before my feet are tired,
May I reach your dwelling-place?
Before I wake from slumber,
You will watch me, Lord, I hold.
Before I throw my mantle
Will you take me in your fold?
Before my work is over,
You, my Lord, will right the wrong.
Before you play your music
Will you let me sing my song?

After the War Inayat Khan Asked Me to Try to Make Contacts for Him in Holland

After the war Inayat Khan asked me to try to make
contacts for him in Holland.
I introduced him in Leiden, where he gave a concert
in the circle of the famous Leiden University.
Professor De Haas and his wife,
daughter of Professor Lorentz,
had always been great admirers of my husband's art.
They invited us to perform during
international congresses.
And so we entered international scientific circles.

They also took great interest in my teaching
based on my studies with Inayat Khan,
and studies of the three Hindu sciences,

176

for which there are no faculties
in Western universities.

1. The Science of Man:
The structure and functioning of the body
as an expressive instrument.

2. The Study of the Phenomenon of Movement.
There I was greatly helped by my husband,
and by four Western scientists:
a. By Arthur Compton's publications on cosmic rays;
b. By Einstein and his discoveries
of the essence of space and relativity;
c. By Eddington's publication on the relation
of past and future;
d. By Professor De Haas and his wife, with whom
I did some simple exercises they executed very well.
3. The Study of Space Functions in the Human Form.
This gave me the opportunity
to find that my discoveries on the spatial skeleton
and its three dimensions,
giving man the possibility of expressing himself
in space in six directions,
were founded on a solid scientific basis.
For Western science states:
"That space is inherent in movement."
This very important scientific fact
which Einstein wished so much to be understood
by all human beings;
was never offered to the understanding
of Western people in general.

Bhimo

Raden Mas Jodjana and I had a son.
Bhimo was his name.
When he was still a baby, my husband told him
the story of "Bhimo", one of five brothers, the Pandavas.
The Hindu epic poem, the Mahabharata,
tells the long story of their race,
and of the struggle between them and the Kuravas
their cousins.

Just after Christ's birth,
the Hindus came to Java as traders.
Then the Javanese heard the tales from the "Mahabharata",
and from another epic poem, the "Ramayana".

177

The people were most impressed
and loved these tales.

They themselves had an ancestral cult.
Long before the Hindus came to Java
they performed shadow plays, called WAYANG.
The shadows were cut out of leather,
painted in beautiful colours and gilded.
The ceremonies and plays were commemorating
the ancestors in respectful remembrance.
The Javanese live in a most intimate communion with the dead.
One month in the year the dead leave their graves.
Then the still living children and grandchildren,
fast and pray and await their return.

The graveyard where Jodjana's and Bhimo's ancestors rest
is a wonderful place.
An immense hall which you reach
first passing through a garden graveyard.

Then entering the house by a smaller, but still spacious room,
you come to the big home
of the great, most honoured parents of the past.
And there, after long training, you can stay
and enter into a state of total oblivion of the self
and become the servant of the Presence in service to the dead.

The Javanese also perform ceremonies and dance prayers
accompanied by a small orchestra, called "GAMELAN".
These dances are performed by the simple peasants on the land
praying to the Gods for an abundant harvest.
They also pray to the beautiful Goddess SHRI.
She visits the rice fields and the barns.
The peasants put flowers and little mirrors in the barns
that SHRI may meet her beauty in those small mirrors,
accept the flowers and then stay on in the barns
helping to bring a good harvest,
plentiful food for all.

When the Hindus came to live in Java,
the Javanese started to create new shadow plays
based on the tales they were told by the Hindus
about the five brothers, the Pandavas.
These plays are still performed,
but have become shows for tourists,
lacking the deep religious essence.
They have become means of exploitation.

There is one mystical play of initiation –
the story of Bhimo's life.

178

This play is a purely Javanese composition.

You will not find its story in the Hindu epic poem, the Mahabharata.
Bhimo in the performance of this sacred play represents the human being.
Its teaching can show us how on this earth
we can become wholly receptive, wholly comprehending,
and reach the state of Being.
The story tells how Bhimo sets out
sent by his master Drono,
to bring some water from the source of life to Drono.

In this mystical play of initiation the Javanese introduced
a shadow, which long before the Hindus came to Java,
played the most important part in the ancient and traditional rites
in the ceremonies of the ancestral cult.
The name of this shadow is SEMAR.
In the play of initiation, he is the master in a group of clowns.

Semar has a strange clownish form.
He is young and old at the same time.
He is man and woman.
He represents the basic faith and wisdom of the Javanese race.
The perfect union of opposites.
The universal law of balance in creation.

The play lasts twelve hours.
It starts at six in the afternoon
when the sun sinks suddenly behind the far horizon.
It ends when the sun rises at six
and quite suddenly it is day.
There is no dusk nor dawn in Indonesia.

Exactly at midnight Semar enters the stage.
He comes to play his part in the process of initiation,
when Bhimo on his way to the fountain of life
arrives at midnight at a dark jungle wood,
in which he knows that two terrible monsters live.
Bhimo hesitates to enter this wood.
This part of the play symbolises the moment in human life
when we discover that we should enter
into inner space, we have so long ignored
and where through our neglect
monsters have grown.
That means the forces which we have through years ill-used,
and which have misformed the structure of our organs and their functions.
The skeleton of the text is in esoteric language,
and uses the most simple terms of everyday speech.
So that the non-initiated public
can and does enjoy the play.
Bhimo turns to Semar and asks:
"Must I enter this forest?"
Semar answers: "*I* do not know."

The initiates know. Semar tells Bhimo:
"*You should know*. You should address yourself
to the presence of Being within yourself.
You must become your true Self."

Bhimo enters the jungle wood.
He is attacked by the two monsters,
he fights and slays them.
They drop and die.
But suddenly their forms vanish,
and where they lay
stand two wonderful heavenly creatures
ready to serve him.

And they lead him out of the wood
to the shore of the ocean,
where Bhimo meets Deva Rutji –
his true Self.
Deva Rutji, the Keeper of the Waters,
a tiny creature carried by the waves of the ocean.
And it is through the ear of Deva Rutji
that Bhimo reaches the fountain of life.

My husband told the story of the young Bhimo to our baby son.
From then on, our son Bhimo, identified himself with the Bhimo in the play,
forgetting that it was a story built on the old traditional initiation.
When our son was not yet three years old, he would say:
"O Mother, tell this lady about my friend the little elephant."
Or, "Mother, tell them that you left me in a ball of skin in the garden."

Bhimo created the basis of this book of self re-education,
without having any consciousness of his extraordinary genius.
This genius was recognized by the excellent French professors
who created an Educational Centre in Clermond-Ferrand,
for the children of people working during the war
in the Underground Movement in France.
At home, I myself prepared the children for the three examinations
in order to allow them to continue their studies at universities.
The professors in Clermond-Ferrand supervised the studies.
They taught and corrected by correspondence
the homework of the children of the members of the resistance movement.
Bhimo never became aware of his own genius.
He always said: "Please Mother, let me stay an ordinary boy."
He was much loved by children,
and very young was always surrounded by little boys and girls.

I just let him be.
And our relationship was wonderful.
He lived united in study and research,
"of how and why things are".
He and his sister Parvati loved to work for their exams.
Never did I have to call them to work.

They started all by themselves every morning at eight o'clock.
It was their joy.
We all made the homework sent to us by the Centre in Clermond-Ferrand,
each of us apart.
Then we compared and teased each other,
when we discovered differences of interpretation –
"Who has made mistakes?"

When working alone in his room
Bhimo used to look out of his window onto the garden,
where his father, Roumah and I worked.
Later on the stone wall outside his window, I found written:
"Here lived Bhimo Jodjana, born on the 16th of January
1924 . . . ."
He died.
We remembered the little dots.

He wrote prose poems in many different languages.
You can find one of them
which he wrote in the English language.

Bhimo knew his fate.
He spoke of it with resignation,
saying: "I will be taken by the enemy. Insh' Allah."
They took him when he went to the Centre for young French students.
His genius was recognized by the French State.
He was a "scholar" from his fourteenth year on.

He was taken by the enemy.
They slowly crushed him and put out the light.

Do remember our dear boy, very beautiful to look at
as those who have met him know.
He was a poet, very musical,
playing many instruments and singing sweet songs
late at night, when he was sitting before the open fire in my room.
His way of moving was very natural and pleasant to look at.
He always gave attention to everything and would say:
"I must find out why and how all things are."
He said it in such a simple way.
Even the peasants among whom we lived whilst hiding from the enemy,
were astonished how well he could do all the work on the land.
They engaged him whenever he was free
and fed him.
He brought home the food to share with us –
there were seven of us, with two babies.
We lost Bhimo when he was eighteen years old.
He will stay in our memory
forever young and beautiful.

Bhimo Jodjana 17 years old in Occupied France, before being taken prisoner.

To a French Soldier

Soldier thou wert
Soldier, who fell
Wondering why – but sure still.
And in that hell
of fire and smoke, of pain and dirt
Suffering, until
Death came.

At the call of war
Thou left thy plough,
Thy home, thy wife
and children sweet.
All thou loved enough
To quit and save their life.
Thy life to give
For human's sake, and for thy love
And then – for France
And for a better world to come.
It was enough.

Deliverance
Yet hasn't come –
Will it some day?
For thou
It has, I hope.
Still earth is hell, and people slay.
Now thou art gone
And still we grope.
For peace – inside and out,
Still more inward,
For outer peace cannot be found,
Nor be without
The peace of heart.

And there thou liest – cold in the ground.
A man thou wert
A man who fell
Wondering why – but sure still.
And in that hell
Of hate and spite, of human dirt
Fighting until
Peace came
And so it will.

Written by Bhimo Jodjana. Age 17.

183

When a Czech Prisoner Came Back Alive from Buchenwald

When a Czech prisoner came back to France alive from Buchenwald,
he came to see me and told me
our son would never return to us.

We had previously received a letter from the Dutch Government,
telling us that Bhimo had died in June 1944.

But afterwards in Buchenwald, the enemy had introduced a boy
to members of the International Red Cross,
telling them that this boy was our son.
The Red Cross were allowed to stay with him for a short time
and write a report on his state of health,
or anything else that was of interest to them.
But they were not allowed to speak to the boy or ask him questions.
And the boy under guard had to stay quite motionless.
So the enemy pretended
that our son was still alive, and in good health.

This report circulated,
and caused me the necessity
of following this clue.
For five years, although feeling all the time
that I was on a false trail,
I went in search from one place to another.

I made too many sad discoveries
about the dehumanization of people.
I became bereft of all illusions.
So-called good people, or bad people
play the same game.

Evolution is not a choice to be good and destroy the bad
and thereby destroy balance.
There is in all the same strife —
to gain power, to impose, to dominate, to exploit.
Evolution creates in all human beings
the taste, the awareness and consciousness of perfection.
The Red Indians in America teach that evolution
calls us from within to enter "The path with the heart",
although the heart is not the seat of balance.

I am of Basque descent.
The scientist, Mr. Owen, tried to find the origin
of that mysterious race.

According to him, I had hidden deep in myself
the basic knowledge of what balance is:
It is the perfect union of opposites.
The same basic knowledge was the genius of the Javanese race.
My husband brought the message of this inborn knowledge
through his art of movement, to the West.

Parvati

Parvati, our youngest daughter
has been deeply touched
by the loss of her father.

Quite young with other children
she played on the instruments of the Javanese orchestra, the Gamelan.
And she danced as a child with great concentration and grace.
But she became more and more influenced
by the surrounding Western world.

Her father felt that she would not,
and could never really live
in the very special atmosphere
in which he breathed, lived and had his being.
He gave up trying in any way to influence her.
But his inner life was so strong,
his art on the stage so deeply moving,
that he became for her the ideal man.
She was so impressed by the greatness of his genius
and the contrasting very simple life he led.

When I met my husband for the first time,
when we discovered what was going to link us forever
in life, and hereafter;
he told me that for the past nine years
he had not shared a single moment
of intimate contact with anyone.
Not spoken one word about his inner life.
Not even with his own people
when he met them in Holland.

Later when we met so many men and women
in different circles of human society, and in different countries,
who showed us warm feelings of admiration, appreciation and "friendship",
Jodjana stayed aloof, trying to find a way of showing
that he was aware of their feelings,
but complaining to me that he did not know
what to speak about with them.

He preferred to stay in "easy-going" company.
He often fell asleep after a meal with friends.
Even in our family, he lived in his studio
coming late to meals, when the children and others first waiting,
had started and nearly finished their meals.
He found one couple "easy going",
"because" as he said, "their inner life
amount to philosophizing."
They only cared about themselves
and did not expect him to bring or add anything to their life,
beyond the enjoyment of being "best friends" with a great artist.

Our little son, Bhimo, was often with him in his studio.
The little boy had a silent understanding with his father.

My husband's emanation became so strong and spread so wide in space,
that when he moved on the stage
great happenings spread in space.
In daily life in many situations, this state protected him,
because it kept people from coming too near.

With my husband, one had to live "in the riverbed"
deeply rooted in being,
from where one could see the undercurrents of a waterway.
He was "branched on the Creator".

He represented all the Gods on the stage.
No one could understand
how it was possible to be a God.
He when asked, said: "One cannot do as if one were a God."
It did not really answer their question.

Some people lived "eternity" during the performances.
They entirely lost the consciousness of time
in this relative world.
After the performance some asked to be allowed
to sit for a while in the dressing-room,
in order not to lose this full consciousness of the Infinite.

The poet, A. Roland Holst, wrote some wonderful thoughts
describing his experience during a performance.

He felt as if my husband made the public
live and see Eternal Being in a mirror.

They broke that wonderful mirror.

When he fell ill, all those around him
took care of him with loving hearts.

186

Most of all our daughter, Parvati
and her husband.
But when he went through terrible ordeals in the hospitals,
he called out to me,
and when I came he said: "I have lost my Self,
Help me, give me back my Self."
Roumah helped me. My husband's health improved, and he hoped to live with us again.
He begged us to take him away,
find him a place where he could live
in and by himself,
we protecting him as we had always done.
But though we obtained permission
to establish him in a home with a garden,
and the promise of doctors to help us
and supervise our nursing him,
circumstances and people caused obstruction.
So all his hope and wishes led to no fulfilment.

He then gave up hoping to find again on earth
this necessary atmosphere
in which "branched on his Creator"
he could breathe and live.

He became totally resigned.
He told us "I have already died.
My bed here is my coffin."

I fell ill.
For sometime we were separated.
We both then lived in the "riverbed".

He then asked me to go to his land and to his people.
I went with Roumah.
But I did not find his home awaiting him.
I tried to awake in his people
the love which by his life he so deserved.
I begged that he might rest
near to his mother.
But there was no response
no understanding whatsoever.
Roumah and I were well received well looked after.
They all co-operated to give us "a good time".
But we despaired.
Still we did our best to show our appreciation
for what they gave and asked no more.

My husband knew from my first letter
that they had received us well.

187

He kept the letter, all the time touching it
and began to tell my daughter happily
about the place where he was born.
And that night, he was even full of joy
in happy remembrance.

The same night – all were asleep –
he died,
went back to his Creator.

Parvati buried the letter, and another letter –
which arrived the morning he passed on –
with him in the cemetery in La Réole,
in the Gironde, in France.

"Sleep well sweet Prince."

Jodjana Gave Blessings to So Many

Jodjana gave blessings to so many
that they might live for a while
carried by divine breath
seeing God as in a mirror.
The presence of Creative Being
was so strong in him,
that he never felt any satisfaction
in his enormous artistic success.
He did not believe
that the enthusiasm of the people
was a success,
for he thought they would then
have become conscious of the Creative Presence,
and that they would have started to show this
in their daily life and conduct.
He stated that this only happened
on very rare occasions.
Every sign of appreciation
for his personal artistic presence
made him extremely humble.
He would always first fold his hands
and retire within himself
before thanking the public for their applause.

We always used to dedicate a performance
to someone who needed to become aware
of being supported by life's breath.
After the death of our dear boy,

188

we dedicated all performances to the dead,
to those whose life had been taken in such a cruel way.

Hoping that the wave of happiness
which the public so gratefully expressed,
might create in space a cosmic condition
benefiting all wherever they might be.
That they might feel that wave of warm human gratitude
for the humble gift of beauty
we had been allowed to manifest.

He used to take my hand and approach the footlights.
We both, then, in our inner being were with the dead
and thanked the public for their gift.

When Jodjana realized that they had killed his son,
and that he would never have another son
to carry on the message, and thus fulfil the promise
the name Jodjana embodies.
(When pronounced the sound of the name
opens the path which my own Basque forefathers
called "the path with the heart")
Jodjana nearly went out of his mind.
Day and night one of us had to stay with him and nurse him.
We could not help him in any other way.
One morning our young daughter, Parvati,
knelt at his bedside and said to him:
"Father, I promise I will do all
Bhimo set out to do."
And she gave up her own wishes and work
and prepared herself to become a doctor of medicine.

Her father recovered,
and in his fifty-third year started on a new "époque" in his career.
Twenty years later he said good-bye to the public
at a performance at the Musée Guimet in Paris.

Roumahlaiselan

Roumahlaiselan is his name.
It means Knight of the house of God.
What a wonderful name!

He came to live with us
more than half a century ago.

We lived on the basis of a teaching
which we applied in daily life.
Passing this teaching on to others
by demonstrating it in performances on the stage.
Those who came to learn,
could not only hear
how they could express themselves
in a creative way,
they could see
how it was done.

The teaching given out thousands of years ago
in the Upanishads and the Bhagavad-Gita,
may perhaps be described thus:
Acting, doing, moving,
must be supported
by the gentle art of
"not-doing".
As all being is merged
in "not-being".

For Roumahlaiselan this teaching represented
the basis of a life spent in humble service
to the Creative Presence,
and to all beings around us.
Our friends often said,
that in him they met
with an angelic presence.
He became a great mime and dancer on the stage
with my husband.
But in our daily surroundings,
throughout all the most humble and necessary duties,
he created and creates in the path with the heart
the most wonderful dance –
the dance of life.

This book could not have been written without the
dedication, love, and utterly devoted service of
Roumahlaiselan to Raden Ayou Jodjana.

Part VIII: Last Poems and Exercises

Through Millions of Years

Through millions of years, evolution has
slowly created through a long series of primates –
Man.
The directions of the movement of this evolutionary process
were backward-downward.

Man was the first creature on this earth
to live in an upright position.

We have arms,
limbs detached from the direct support of the earth,
and, for balance sake able to swing in opposite directions
in accompaniment to the forward movements of the legs.

Our arms should never lose their inborn sense
of trying to find support.
They can find support in the articulations
of the upper armbones inside the shoulder-blades;
in the elbow-joints, and underneath the outer wrist-bones.
Here we find again
that the perfect union of two opposite directions
creates balance.
In many movements in daily life,
such as the knees bending forward in all movements of the legs,
you need the backward support of the elbow joints.

Man in his greed using his arms and hands
to grasp, to grab, to hold,
loses the natural consciousness which created him in an upright position;
and the inborn feeling in the arms seeking support
by a movement in backward direction in the elbow joints.

When an Infant is Born

When an infant is born into this world,
a unique little creature
has passed the threshold of his mother's womb.
During nine months it developed
through a great many stages of the animal kingdom.
It was carried by water from the oceans
which once covered the earth,
and in which the very first forms
of the vegetable and animal kingdoms
developed.

193

The infant enters into this world
on a small wave,
which helps to carry it
to its special destiny –
to become a human being.

This process of evolution has taken countless ages,
and is still going on in every infant.
But the process is far from being achieved.
There have been peaks of achievements –
great prophets, and masters,
artists and scientists of genius
have been among us.
We possess sacred scriptures,
monuments of astounding beauty,
of wisdom and knowledge.
Great works of art,
all revealing the same ultimate truth,
all bringing the same message,
all clearly pointing the way –
how to set out,
to become a true human being.

The Wisdom of the Body

When we leave the body of our mother,
and are born into this world,
hands touch us and put us
in a bed, on the floor, in a cradle.

And this is our first experience in this world.
Experience by the touch of supports.
From birth on, in every moment,
our small limp body absorbs
bodily consciousness of supports.
Feeling and awareness of supports
begins to become alive in every fibre of the body.
Support in the bed,
in the arms of our mother.
We feel warm when we touch her skin
and find food.
We feel the water in the bathtub,
the touch of her hands, and her arm which holds us.
We start to touch our own little body with our hands.
We feel the cold when the season changes.

In the beginning we become conscious of how we are carried.

In the cradle we begin to move,
to sit up.
We crawl on the floor on hands and feet.
Then we try to stand up on our small feet,
to stand in upright position like those around us.
Our hands grasp for support.
Our feet plant themselves firmly on the ground.
We find, or do not find support.
We drop and tumble
and ever start again.

At last we stand up on our feet.
And our *body* begins to *know*
all these experiences,
never to forget them.
There is no brain control
or supervision from the brain-cells.
The brain absorbs the feeling and awareness in the body.
What happens in the body, mirrors
in the tender membranes
around the brain-cells.

The two sides of the centres of attention,
low in the border of the skull,
begin to absorb all these feelings.
The process of self-consciousness is born.
Ever so slowly it develops.
But in the body there is already
direct knowledge of the adventure
which life taught us from birth on.
This is the wisdom of the body.

"The Now and Here"

We in the "Now and Here"
are alive in this world.
We know it,
and we also know
that we are alive because of space workings
inside our body.
And that space is an Infinite Essence.
We can easily understand
that Infinite Space working in us
needs an infinite organ —
a point.

Life's working in us is a basic function
and creates balance in our form
in every "Now".
This function takes place without interruption on the flow of time.
The flow of time in our form works duration.
It works Eternity.
Time being a space working –
a working of Infinity.
Thus our form reveals and manifests
this working in all our substances.
So our physical body becomes the manifestation
of this basic movement,
which causes us to be,
and to become visible
as a living being in every "Now and Here".

The Now and Here are One in Time and Space

"Now and Here" are one in time and space.
"Now" is the acceptance of the breath of life,
restoring in us the total receptivity of the body
by a movement backward to the strong part of our body.
There in the present moment, the future meets the past.
We then create the at-onement of the "Now and Here",
and the birth of the consciousness of the supports.

For most of us it is easier to begin with the "Here".
We can more easily become aware
of where we are in the moment
through the physical contact
of the different parts of our body
which touch supports when sitting,
or during movements:
such as standing on the floor, the ground, the earth,
or leaning against the back of the chair,
our arms sustained by the arms of the chair
and feeling the ground beneath our feet.
Then we can say: "I am here standing on the ground",
or "We are now sitting in our chair".
Then we have the clear awareness of being in the moment
in the "Now",
and from there we can begin all our actions and movements,
all our expressions in acts, in sound, and speech.
This will help us to practise in any moment we choose,
to play, to be, to live.

Never Push, Never Lift

Modern man lifts his stomach, his heart, the borders of his diaphragm, and his shoulders,
and disturbs life's basic function in the cerebellum;
pushing forward and forcing the brain to contract
underneath the front part of the skull above the eyes.
These contractions disarrange the motor centres in the cerebellum,
and the facial muscles.

When moving forward the head usually juts out,
and the upper body pushes in a forward direction.
The weight pulls the body downwards
out of the upright position of the 'human being',
back into the state of the primates,
forcing the body into contracting other muscles
in order to keep it from losing its balance
and dropping.

Man's brain deteriorates,
and returns to the state of an animal
and even worse.
Man becomes a killer and a beast.

"The Song of the Earth" by Gustave Mahler

When we awake in the morning,
we feel descending in the small plane in the backside of our form,
the working of the tender bundling
of the five perpendicular lines.

Then life starts to happen
in our waking consciousness,
while we go on descending
to the well of Life;
from where we are united
to all forms in the Universe,
and we are given the never-failing support of the Earth.

Then we consciously feel
how the working of the rising movement mounts.
We become aware of the rising movement
which created us upright.

And we listen, deeply moved
to the "Song of the Earth",
once created by a human being.

197

The song mounting in him from the well of Life
and going out into Infinite Space,
forever, forever, forever. . . .

This Song mounts in all human beings,
in all Nature,
in water, in trees, in the air,
in the world of stars, and beyond
forever, forever, forever. . . .

Never finding the "tonic"
no beginning, no ending.
It carries and rocks us gently
forever, forever, forever. . . .

The Essence of Love

My "i" being sorry for you
can, and does not help you.
Pity is not Love!

Asking for attention for one's pains and sorrows,
does not awaken Love in others.
From both sides there should only be
conscious tender acceptance of the other's troubles
and the awakening of Love's radiance.

Even a slight opening from the centre of balance suffices.
As soon as space-working is freed in us
the personally narrowed "i" is evaporating,
disappearing, dying,
and Love radiates tenderly in the whole form
and illuminates the body.

The Tide is Out

The tide is out
and carries me on,
and at the same time, backward.

It is not so long ago
that I came down along a pathway from the dunes,
and stood on England's south-coast,
on a small sandy beach.

The incoming tide only left a small strip of sand.
The air and the sea were gently breathing.
Nobody near.
No trace or sound of human being,
of human life.
The sunny air was warm.
And the sea wide open towards the horizon,
on each breath caressing the beach
and gently nearing my feet on the sand.

My own breath came in and out
on the rhythm of the gently waving waters.
I opened to the incoming tide. . . .
And see . . . the tide changes,
hesitates a few moments,
and then goes out.

Like there on England's south-coast
I am standing on the coast of life.
The tide hesitates again. . . .
The tide is out.

From the Depth of Being

From the depth of being
I thank you, gentle people.

Gentle people, already around me.
And you, friends, still to come
to that small sandy strip of beach,
where once I saw the tide change and go out.
Thanks to you all who came,
and to you who will come.

I cannot call you, cannot ask you to come.
Because those who are, and live under orders
like Inayat Khan, like my busband,
like our dear son Bhimo;
we have to live on the pure gift
of those who come listening to the call of love
in their own heart.

This Book Comes to its End

This book comes to its end.
It is the outcome of research;
a very simple research in our own body
as the Upanishads advise us to do.

Everyone has a right,
perhaps a duty and necessity
to start on his own inner research,
acting according to his own inner inspiration.
Because inspiration is not an occult phenomenon,
but a very real basic function in our body.
Inspiration is the creative breath
forming the body.
This breath keeps the body alive;
it reveals "what" and "how" we are.
Thus we should understand the meaning
of what we call inspiration.
This creative breath
carries all our actions and expressions.
It is a real breath, a real function in our form.

So fare-thee-well, all of you.
I loved you as my fellows on the path of life.
I leave you this book
as a token of love.
This love which moves the universe.

May it help you to achieve
what you were meant to fulfil.
Fare-thee-well!